MARCONI
FATHER OF RADIO

MARCONI
FATHER OF RADIO

by David Gunston

with drawings by Eric J. Woodley

Crowell-Collier Press   •   New York

Contents

1
Communications before Marconi

There have been many great sieges in world history, but one of the first is still among the most famous: the siege of Troy. Then a flourishing city in Asia Minor, Troy was the focal point of the long and bitter quarrel between the Trojans and the Ancient Greeks. Although the Greek armies besieged Troy for nearly ten years, they could not take the stronghold by force, and so had to resort to cunning. If we are to believe Homer and Virgil, the ruse they used was that of the famous Trojan Horse.

About 1184 BC Troy fell to the valiant Greeks, led by Odysseus (Ulysses) their hero, with Agamemnon, King of Mycenae, as commander-in-chief. The idea was simple: a great horse was made out of wood, big enough to hold 100 soldiers, but purporting to be a peace-offering to the Greek goddess Athena. The Greek forces were to return to their ships, leaving only the small, picked force hidden inside the effigy outside the well-defended gates of Troy. The mock evacuation was carried out under cover of darkness, and the Greek ships sailed away.

When the Trojans discovered the horse and the absence of their enemies, they naturally rejoiced at their good fortune. The monster was dragged inside the city, many hours were spent in celebrations, but finally the exhausted Trojans fell asleep, confident that they were victorious. Then the Greek soldiers descended from their hiding-place, opened the gates

7

of Troy and let in thousands of their comrades who meanwhile had landed from the ships that turned back towards Troy after they had vanished from the sight of the Trojans. Before long Troy was over-run with ferocious Greek troops who massacred their enemies and pillaged the city until by morning only smoking ruins remained. With total victory theirs, the war-weary Greeks made ready to return to the homeland and the families they had not seen for almost ten years. The siege of Troy was over.

This famous story has of course been told and re-told many times since it took place in those far-off days, often with embellishments added later. But two incidents in it are of especial interest to us today.

First, when the Greek soldiers penetrated the strongly-defended city in their horse, they had to have some way of telling their fellows still in the galleys out at sea that the trick had worked, signalling them to land immediately, before the tired Trojans awoke with the dawn. This they did, quite successfully, in the only way they knew how in the darkness. They lit a fire on or outside the great walls. Directly its beacon light was visible out at sea, the main force moved inshore.

Secondly, like modern military commanders, Agamemnon realized that the morale of his troops was highly important, particularly since they had all been away from home for so long. He knew that their thoughts were more with those they had left behind than on the ultimate fate of Troy. He knew, too, that the Greeks at home waited long and anxiously for news of the siege and of their loved ones taking part in it. Unfortunately, many miles of wild, rocky country separated the two groups, so that even the fleetest messengers on horse or foot would take days, if not weeks, to carry any news back to Greece. So Agamemnon hit upon a swifter plan to tell the homeland when Troy fell, as he was confident it would. He had long known the usefulness of a single beacon fire for long-distance signalling, especially at night. Now he devised an extension of this simple basic idea. He ordered large beacon fires to be laid on the tops of Mounts Ida, Athos, and Cithaeron, and on smaller intervening peaks. Beside each pyre he had reliable watchers working on a shift system day and night long before the siege approached its final stages. These men had strict orders always to keep their eyes directed towards Troy, to watch for the big blaze that would announce the capture of the city. When at last this happened, bringing victory to the clever Greeks, beacon after beacon sprang into signalling flame all along the route back to within sight of Greece. Thus was the glad news speedily sent to the homeland, to Agamemnon's own wife, Queen Clytemnestra, and the waiting wives and children of the weary Greek soldiers.

Now the interesting thing is that although Agamemnon was a skilled military leader and a clever man, neither he nor his aides could think of any other better way of sending the long-awaited news back home with the minimum of delay. He had to use the primitive but admittedly effective method of communicating by fire, a trick known since cave-man days. Pre-arranged fire or smoke signals had been used to convey urgent news over a distance by the Ancient Egyptians and the Assyrians before the Trojan War, and of course they were to be used for a great many centuries afterwards. The towers all along the Great Wall of China, which was built about 200 BC to keep the nomadic Tartars out of the country, were designed to be able to signal to one another by beacon fires on their tops, as well as for simple look-out purposes. When the great Spanish Armada sailed on England in AD 1588, beacon fires were used all along the Channel coast to give warning of the threatened attack. Many similar fires were built (but not lit) to give warning of the next attempted invasion of Britain, by the Germans in 1940, and the practice of sending dire or glad news by fire lingers on, if only in the custom of lighting celebration bonfires on special occasions.

The truth is that man has always felt the need to 'talk at a

9

distance'. Very early indeed in human history, once the basic needs of food and shelter were met, perhaps even before, men have been aware of the urge to communicate with their fellows. Sign language, mere miming and gesticulation, came first, to be followed by vocal noises like grunts of satisfaction, chuckles of pleasure, yells of glee or fear, threatening or warning shouts, before coherent speech came into being. A great many members of the human race still communicate with one another with hand signs, if only to support or extend speech: all of us do to some extent. But as human life came to be better organized into tribes and small villages or camps, communication by word or gesture, although essential, was not enough. The necessity of being able to get in touch with others who lived at a distance was clearly recognized.

From that moment on, the so-called science of communications was born – a science that was to develop with very slow and painful steps for many centuries, until our own, in fact. In the main, communication was carried out either by travelling to the distant folk oneself, or by sending messengers. The actual art of communication had not really advanced at all: you merely spoke to the distant people after you had journeyed to them, or maybe sent a written message by someone else. Only in battle, when disaster threatened or urgency became all-important, was there much attempt to communicate by quicker, more direct means. Talking at a distance began out of the need to go one better than one's enemies.

The much-tried use of fire or smoke was probably the most widely-used of all primitive signalling methods, although it had its dangers and drawbacks, not least of which being that the enemy very often got the message too! The North American Indians perfected this technique, using smoke rings or puffs by day, and fire-arrows by night. The smoke signals were regulated by building a fire of moist materials on flat ground or in a hollow, and placing a blanket or robe over it. When the covering was smartly pulled away, smoke rose on windless days in a conspicuous ring or puff, to be immediately noted by other Redskins afar off. As is necessary with almost all kinds of long-distance signalling, a simple code had to be devised. For instance, one puff might mean: LOOK OUT! ENEMY NEAR; two puffs: WE INTEND TO CAMP HERE; and three puffs: I AM IN DANGER. SEND HELP. Fire-arrows were shot off at night for the same purpose.

As short-distance and world communications are so highly efficient and commonplace today we find it hard to believe that they grew so slowly. Yet it is a fact that no really effective method of improving on the spoken or written message carried by foot, horse, wheeled vehicle or water-borne craft over long distances came into general use until the nineteenth century. Many attempts were made to find one: most of them seem to us today to be absurd or hopelessly primitive or limited. Nevertheless, for by far the bulk of mankind's history, these methods were all people could use to communicate with others out of normal earshot. In any case, simple signalling was early recognized as being quite inadequate. As one historian has put it: 'Human thought required a system which could convey *more than one idea*.' It required it desperately, yet for so many hundreds of years it was unable to devise it.

Some authorities consider that marine signalling was the first kind of long-distance communication to receive serious attention away from the use of crude beacon fires. We read in the tales of Ancient Greece how Theseus, one of the Argonauts who sought the Golden Fleece, invented for an earlier expedition a system of flying coloured sails on his ship to convey a message. Unfortunately he caused the death of his aged father, Aegeus, by his failure to handle his signals properly. When setting out for his adversary, Theseus flew black sails on his ship, and it was arranged that if he was victorious, white sails of victory would be flown on the return journey. Owing to an unexpected distraction, he forgot to change his sails later, and although he returned successful from his encounter, Aegeus

saw the black sails and, thinking his son had been killed, was
so upset that he threw himself into the sea – still called the
Aegean Sea, after him.

A legend, of course; but it shows us another simple form of
signalling for ships that was in use in early times. No major
advance from signalling at sea by sails or flags came until the
invention of gunpowder in the sixteenth century, when
cannon shots could be used for inter-ship communication.

Meanwhile, many ingenious but not very efficient devices
had to be used. There was the 'clepsydra', a signalling varia-
tion of the primitive water clock. A tall glass tube was erected
in a kind of tower and filled with water. A float carrying a
light was placed on the water, and crude messages were sent
over a distance by setting the light at certain levels by either
letting out some of the water at the bottom of the tube, or
filling it up higher. Each level indicated a pre-arranged message, and the tower was high enough for these to be judged
with some accuracy from afar. In the Vatican, in Rome, is a
drawing of a strange device called a 'stentorophonic tube',
said to have been invented by Alexander the Great. Rather
like a gigantic megaphone, it was said to carry the human
voice up to 12 miles.

But signalling with sound was never very satisfactory, and
visual methods were most widely used and experimented
with. Sometimes these were comparatively simple, like the
different coloured tunics, spears or shields worn by warriors
to pass on messages to nearby groups in daytime. Others were
more ingenious, like the polished mirrors and metal shields
used as heliographs by both the Ancient Greeks and the
Egyptians to reflect the sun's rays in message form. It is said
that messages were flashed like this at the Battle of Marathon,
about 490 BC; but the heliograph proper, with its adjustable
mirror mounted on a tripod, was not perfected until about
1870, when the invention of the Morse Code had made signalling with short or long flashes of light simple. Another recent

adaptation of the same idea is found in electric signalling lamps, like the Aldis lamp, still widely used at sea, with their worthwhile range of some 4 miles by day and 12 miles by night.

But until the seventeenth century, at least, these methods of communication were exceptional rather than general. Most messages, short as well as long, reached their destination if not by unaided human feet, then with the help of horse, coach or sailing ship. There was, in fact, no other way, and long delays were inevitable. This largely accounts for the much slower pace of life in bygone centuries compared with the bustle of today. Even wars might be lost or won in distant parts without the people at home knowing anything about them until months later. The Greeks, Romans, and Aztecs were only some of the earlier civilizations to use relays of fleet-footed couriers (literally, 'runners') to pass on messages from one town or settlement to another. Each man ran full out for the length of his appointed route, then shouted or handed the tidings to the next – a basic system of communication that seems laughable today but which in fact was later developed into the stage coach and Pony Express systems of more recent centuries. One Persian king of ancient times even thought of having stationary sentinels spaced out for miles, each shouting the message on to the next; and the Gauls copied the idea. According to Caesar, the news of the massacre of the Romans at Orleans was transmitted in this way to the more southerly French province of Auvergne, a distance of some 150 miles.

But of course although this method of talking at a distance was quicker than the others, it needed vast numbers of very patient and reliable men and was open to every possible chance of error and misunderstanding. It reminds one of the amusing old British Army story of the simple message: PLEASE SEND REINFORCEMENTS, WE ARE GOING TO ADVANCE which, when passed along a short line of troops, reached its destination as: PLEASE SEND THREE-AND-FOURPENCE, WE

13

ARE GOING TO A DANCE.

In 1684, the prolific English inventor and physicist Robert Hooke devised a new signalling device which he thought would be useful for moderate distances over land or sea. This consisted of a large black board on a frame with 24 movable white stencils representing the letters of the alphabet (I and V being omitted). Any message could be spelled out by bringing the stencils into position in front of the board, but this somewhat slow and laborious idea was later developed into the swifter semaphore, which used a simple letter code for the various positions of its two movable arms (once as long as 10–12 ft.) on an upright post. Similar, too, is the hand semaphore system, or 'wig-wag', as learnt by Boy Scouts and still practised in the world's navies. A good naval semaphore signaller, holding his two small flags, can achieve a speed of up to 15 words a minute.

Nautical signalling generally developed the use of larger signal flags once heavy signal sails were found too cumbersome. Various British sailors of the eighteenth century worked on the idea of using coloured signal flags for either letters of the alphabet or complete words: it was left to the famous sailor-novelist Captain Frederick Marryat to work out the most efficient system that would enable all kinds of messages to be sent and received at sea. His method was modified into the International Signal Code, as is used all over the world today, which requires 40 separate flags. This Code came into general use in 1887, and was followed by the still-used method of weather signalling with black cones by day, and three lamps arranged triangle-fashion by night.

Some time before marine signalling reached universally-understood perfection, men in the nineteenth century began to feel ever more strongly the need for improved methods of communication. This became more pressing as methods of transport improved. With the arrival of the railway train, for instance, some foolproof way had to be found of making sure drivers stopped when this was necessary. In the very early days of railways men actually stood at fixed points along the track, holding up large square boards. To stop a train a man would turn his board to face the oncoming engine: if all was clear, he kept his board parallel with the line. This crude system was later replaced with a semaphore signal, which still survives on many lines today, save that the single hinged arm with a lamp at one end is raised or lowered at a distance by the signalman in his box.

It is interesting to note, too, that sound signalling has by no means died out completely, even though it must always be of limited range and usefulness. In fog on railways, small explosive detonators placed on the permanent way warn engine-drivers of danger and tell them to stop, while sirens and fog-horns are vital contributors to safety at sea, especially when visibility is bad. If lighthouses and buoys still send their warning (or identification) messages in a way that is many thousands of years old, they also make use of sound as well, signalling to passing ships by hooter, diaphone, or bell. Nor should we forget the sometimes very necessary communicating noise of the fire-engine or ambulance bell or siren, nor the motor-car horn or bicycle bell!

Until the beginning of the nineteenth century, however, every form of human communication made use of forces or materials that had long been known. Now, at long last, there began to cross men's minds the possibility of harnessing not a new force (for it had been known since ancient times) but a force about which human knowledge was growing in a surprising fashion – electricity. It seemed to a few advanced minds that this almost magical force, with its power of rushing along a conductor wire, might be made to spell out messages at a distance, provided the wire was long enough.

Although electricity was still largely regarded as a kind of fascinating toy or plaything, serious-minded men were gradually unveiling its true powers. In 1799, the Italian scientist

15

Volta made the first electrical cell battery, the successors of which enabled experimenters to push on with their at first fairly vague notions of some sort of electric semaphore or telegraph. Hitherto current had to be generated laboriously by the hand-turning of a large wheel on a friction-machine, and then stored precariously inside the simple condenser of a glass Leyden jar. Then, between 1820 and 1831 came the momentous discoveries of Oersted, in Denmark, and Faraday, in England, concerning the magnetic properties of electric currents, notably how a magnetized compass needle may be made to deflect either one way or the other, according to the direction of flow of the current in a wire placed close and parallel to it.

Here, at last, was a way of sending a simple message-carrying electric charge along a wire. It did not need a great deal of ingenuity to see that a code could be worked out using various numbers of deflection each way to represent letters of the alphabet.

Even so, progress was not speedy. An English inventor called Ronald had already (in 1816) devised a pithball tele-graph which signalled by making two little pith balls diverge when a current was passed along the wire holding them, but this required a separate wire for each letter of the alphabet, and moreover, was still powered by frictional electricity. Remembering this, the subsequent experimenters tried to reduce the number of wires needed to transmit a word-message, and ran their crude telegraphs from reliable cell batteries.

At Göttingen University, in Germany, two science profes-sors, Gauss and Weber, adapted Michael Faraday's magneti-cally-revolved disc to their design of simple telegraph, sending a signal along a wire by moving a magnetic key. But the first really practical telegraph appeared in 1837, the fruit of much work by two Englishmen, Sir William Cooke and Professor Charles Wheatstone. They reduced the wires needed to five,

16

which operated five needles. Two needles operated at a time, pointing to a letter of the alphabet, which was arranged in a diamond pattern. By reversing the direction of the current in the wires, they showed it was possible to point at will to any letter, and so spell out a message.

What was particularly interesting about this invention was the use Wheatstone and Cooke made of a discovery made the previous year by another German, Karl Steinheil, of Munich. This was to use the earth to complete the return circuit of the electric current used, then a revolutionary principle, but of course now universal with electrical apparatus. Steinheil had in fact produced his own form of telegraph in that year, using only two wires and two needles. He fixed metal attachments to the latter, so that when they were magnetically deflected they struck gongs or bells of different notes.

Thus this telegraph, too, could send a message, but although it was later improved to have the needles fixed to ink-holders in contact with a moving paper tape, which meant that a series of two parallel lines of marks or dots could be trans-mitted according to a pre-arranged code, Steinheil's machine did not work so well in practice as did the British discovery. Four years after this was invented, it was placed on public exhibition only as a mildly interesting novelty. Its two inventors, however, were convinced of its usefulness, and by 1845 had so improved their apparatus that only a single wire was necessary.

Meanwhile, back in 1837, a versatile American named Samuel Morse was following up lines of his own in relation to electro-magnetic telegraphy. He had been convinced five years earlier that it was possible, and was sure the best method was not to use deflected magnetic needles at all, but simply to 'sound' out the message along the wire by interrupting the current momentarily with a hand-operated 'key'. All that was needed was to differentiate between short or long sounds, which he termed 'dots' and 'dashes' – and have a simple code

17

to work from. With his colleague Alfred Vail, he devised the famous Code that bears his name in the same year that Wheatstone and Cooke brought out their telegraph in London, and in addition produced an efficient 'sounder' telegraph to operate it, with longer wires and much stronger batteries than had previously been used. In 1838, he was telegraphing over a distance of 10 miles, and his fellow-countrymen were so impressed that their Government began to take notice of Morse's achievement. As one spectator at this test observed, perhaps a trifle optimistically: 'Time and space are now annihilated.'

By 1843, official support was forthcoming, and whereas the two Englishmen had to be content with demonstrating their telegraph system over the short distance between the two London districts of Chalk Farm and Euston, Morse was fortunate enough to be voted $30,000 by Congress to build an experimental telegraph line between the towns of Washington and Baltimore, a distance of about 36 miles. On 24 May 1844, the first message travelled along this line. It read: WHAT HATH GOD WROUGHT? As each letter was spelt out on the tapper, or key, at one end of the line, an electro-magnet at the other end reacted to the varying impulses by moving up and down against stops, so making a clicking noise easily read by ear when sent slowly.

Since then, of course, countless messages in Morse Code have winged their way around the globe. Its great advantages were simplicity, and the ease with which it could be adapted by other apparatus than Morse's own sounder. It worked equally well with the needle telegraph, since a deflection one way signified a dot, and the other way a dash. Later, too, it was to be used equally well with radio signalling.

Although both needle and sounder telegraphs were soon greatly improved and widely used for many years, it became increasingly evident that they were too slow and too limited to be of universal use. Even when Morse brought out his self-recording telegraph, which inked out the dots and dashes it

18

received, it was clear that to be of real commercial value a telegraph, with its miles of costly wires, must work faster than anything yet seen and carry several messages at a time. Very many devices were thought up to these ends, culminating in the high-speed teleprinter and the so-called 'voice-frequency' systems used today, which employ up to 18 message channels on a single line, each on its own signalling frequency.

But back in the middle of the last century these improvements were still in the future: men were amazed at the simplest telegraphed message, and work began in both Europe and America to lay endless miles of overhead lines and, after 1850, even longer lines of submarine cables. With the first successful linking of the Transatlantic cable in 1858, even though it was to fail after only three months, men could really be said to be able to talk at a great distance.

Yet so far the talking could be done only in code using electrical impulses along a wire. It was infinitely quicker than sending a messenger on foot or horse, or by any other known means of transport, though still very costly. But it was still a limited form of human communication. The human voice could not be sent by telegraph, and it is the human voice, above all else, that really completes human communication.

It was not until 1876 that the human voice was first transmitted intelligibly along an electric wire with the successful invention of the telephone, by a Scotsman who later became a naturalized American, Alexander Graham Bell. On 11 March in that year, in an hotel in Boston, USA, where he was experimenting, Bell himself spoke those first telephone words to his assistant, Thomas A. Watson, who was in another part of the building: MR WATSON. COME HERE; I WANT YOU. Bell had made a long study of acoustics and speech, as well as of electro-magnetism, and he developed the basically simple idea of causing spoken sound waves acting on a sensitive, flexible mouthpiece diaphragm to produce variable electric currents in the transmitting wire. On reaching a second dia-

19

phragm in the earpiece at the receiving end, these currents were made magnetically to reproduce the sound waves that caused them originally. Although the modern telephone instrument and its traffic handling are vastly improved since Bell's day, his fundamental principles remain largely unchanged.

Up to this point, however, although audible speech began to be transmitted electrically, both telegraphy and telephony were limited by their wires and all the costly and troublesome paraphernalia of poles, brackets, mountings, insulators and cables that had to be installed wherever communication was needed. Of course, we still do rely heavily upon wires and cables, particularly for our modern telephone services, but the limitations of wire-carried messages are obvious.

Although only a very few scientific minds began to consider it, the time was growing ripe for a complete breakthrough in electrical communication. What was needed was a completely new and untapped medium for the transmission of human thoughts and desires, and it was not long before one was discovered. The growing pace of industrial life with its innumerable applications of recent scientific discoveries in the latter half of the nineteenth century really made the discovery of this new communications medium essential. Just as physical communications grew more and more wonderful and efficient—steamships instead of sail, steam engines instead of horse-drawn coaches, and soon the momentous discovery of the internal combustion engine with its astonishing application first to road and then to air transport – so the need for an instantaneously speedy, time- and space-less method of talking at a distance became ever more urgent. All that was required was to do away with the wires and cables.

The idea of the possibility of telegraphing without wires had been mooted as long before as 1838 by Karl Steinheil, but the new medium was first hit upon in 1865 by the brilliant Scottish physicist, James Clerk Maxwell, working at that time in King's College, London. He proved *by mathematical calculation*, not by experiment, that there must exist in space electromagnetic waves which, although invisible, behave in the same way as light and travel at the same speed, 186,000 miles per second. He further showed that waves of light are in fact waves of electrical and magnetic force. Maxwell was unable to produce these mysterious waves, nor was he aware that they were, in fact, just the communicating medium men required, namely, wireless waves.

It was not until 1887 that these waves were produced and detected under controlled conditions. The man responsible was a young German mathematician and physicist, Heinrich Hertz, working in his laboratory at the Karlsruhe Polytechnic, and his contribution to the discovery of radio cannot be over-estimated.

Hertz rigged up his quite simple apparatus, consisting of two large flat coils of wire, each with a gap in them arranged between two metal knobs, or electrodes. He then passed a powerful current from a condenser battery through one coil, noticing that an electric spark leapt across the gap when the voltage used was high enough. The effect of this spark, he noted, was to disturb the air in the gap by setting up, or inducing, currents that bounced, or as he said, oscillated, between the knobs. This apparatus he therefore called an oscillator. In addition, he had an identical piece of equipment, not connected to the first, which he set up a little way away. When the oscillator coil was sparking merrily from the current in the battery, he noticed that a corresponding sparking was instantly set up between the electrode knobs of the second coil. Clearly, some powerful though invisible force was bridging the distance between the two coils, and when Hertz increased this, even putting each coil in a separate room in the building, the effect was still the same. The second apparatus, which he called a resonator, still picked up some form of powerful electric vibrations given off by the first spark and

21

which were strong enough to cause a duplicate display of sparking. He knew then that he had discovered, inside his own work-room, the very waves that Maxwell had said existed. There was from his first coil an oscillatory discharge of potent electrical energy that not only jumped the gap in the form of sparks but also radiated outwards in the form of waves. He himself described the results of this experiment as 'the outspreading of electric force'.

Hertz realized that his discovery was of major importance and suggested that these mysterious electro-magnetic waves, like light waves, must travel in a strange, non-material, air-less medium, the 'universal medium' of the ether (or aether), since they passed equally well through a vacuum and so did not need air to move through. He discovered that his waves and light waves did in fact travel at the same incredibly high speed that Maxwell had foretold, deducing that light waves did themselves consist of electrical vibrations in the ether.

With the knowledge that this all-pervading medium of the ether would carry electric waves anywhere at the speed of light, that such waves could be set up by the discharge of a spark across a spark-gap in a coil and, most important of all, that the same waves could then be received in another, similar coil 'in resonance' with the first, it was clear at last that the establishment of some form of wire-*less* telegraphy was not far away.

These first wireless waves were initially known as Hertzian waves, after their discoverer, but when the great British scientist, Lord Kelvin, was translating into English the German account of these important experiments, he termed them 'ether-waves'. Incidentally, it is worth noting that in a field of human discovery so complex and far-reaching as radio, no one man can be said to have discovered all the important things, and Hertz himself was much inspired and aided by Kelvin's own investigations into the electro-magnetic dis-charges of the Leyden jar some twenty years earlier.

22

To record his waves in motion, and to aid his calculations of their length and velocity, Hertz had developed a primitive detecting device based on the discovery some years before by the English inventor, David Edward Hughes, that if a spark was discharged close to a tube of zinc and silver filings, these would cling together to form an electric conductor for as long as the spark was sustained. In 1890, Edouard Branly, a physics professor at the Catholic University in Paris, improved the detector still further and produced a highly sensitive gadget which became known as the coherer, from the way the metallic filings fused together, or cohered. The coherer was to be a highly important piece of early radio equipment, often being used as a switch to operate a bell or relay when the waves impinging upon it made it start conducting current.

The waves Hertz had produced travelled a distance measurable in yards only, and they were very short in length, not much more than an inch or so, while the apparatus he used was primitive in the extreme. But they were sufficiently exciting to stimulate interest in several countries, including Britain, the USA, Russia, Italy, Germany, and France, chiefly as a telegraphing or signalling medium. In Britain, the famous scientist Sir Oliver Lodge was (independently of Branly) working on a coherer for detecting the waves and puzzling the best way of tuning a wireless telegraphy circuit so that it would respond only to a particular frequency of signal waves, and communications engineer Sir William Preece, who had experimented in 1885 with Morse type telegraphy between the mainland and the Isle of Wight, was pursuing his own investigations, especially with a view to improving warnings of gales to lightships at sea. In the USA, where Bell continued his work in communicating the spoken word, others were profiting from his perfection of the telephone receiver, finding in it just the instrument of extreme sensitivity they required to detect minute wave-currents, notably the formidably inventive mind of Thomas A. Edison, who had already successfully

23

achieved a wire-less telegraph system between railway stations and moving trains. The principal Russian scientist groping for a solution to the various problems that still prevented unfettered wireless communication was Professor A. Popoff, who in particular saw the value of the coherer in long-distance communication, while in Italy, at the University of Bologna, Professor Augusto Righi had long been studying Hertzian waves, some of them shorter than those Hertz had produced. A few equally questing minds were similarly at work in Germany, France, and elsewhere.

Although all these men naturally benefited from the earlier work of other investigators, they all saw the need for both original thought and careful experiment. They realized that before wireless could succeed, a number of vital questions had to be satisfactorily answered. For example: Exactly how could oscillations be made to carry an understandable signal? How could oscillations set up by a spark transmitter be reliably detected at a distance? How could the length of the waves used be varied, and a wanted wavelength be isolated from unwanted ones? And how far could these mysterious waves be made to travel?

The practical answers to most of these problems were close at hand, but unexpectedly from none of those expert scientists just mentioned. They were to come from the vision, skill and persistence of a shy, rather lonely young Irish-Italian of twenty-one. Although these men knew nothing of him or his work he knew all about theirs, and for years past had studied their discoveries with intense interest.

It was the spring of 1895, and on his father's extensive estate at Pontecchio, eleven miles outside the ancient Italian city of Bologna, he had unaided built apparatus that was achieving proper wireless communication over distances of half a mile, and then of two miles.

His name, soon to become synonymous with radio itself, was Guglielmo Marconi.

24

2

The Young Experimenter

Guglielmo (or William) Marconi was born on 25 April 1874, at the time when Bell was trying to perfect the invention of the telephone at the University of Boston, USA. Unlike many great scientific discoverers, his origins were neither lowly nor uncomfortable, for his father, dignified Giuseppe Marconi, was a retired businessman, landowner, and man of means who had managed his affairs so successfully that he had amassed quite a fortune. But when he married in 1855 his wife died after giving birth to their first child in the same year.

For nine years he lived with his aged father, a lonely widower with a small son, then he met a pretty Irish girl and in 1864, in spite of the objections of her parents, he married her. She was Annie Jameson, fourth and youngest daughter of Andrew Jameson, one of the founders of a famous whisky distilling firm, a typically stern Victorian. Annie was charming, affectionate, vivacious, a striking contrast to the rather stolid, rigid-minded North Italian who became her husband, but like most of his compatriots, she was very musical. In fact, it was her interest in music that led her to Italy and to the seemingly unlikely, but actually very happy and fruitful union with Giuseppe Marconi. She had a very fine singing voice, but her parents, horrified at the thought she might sing in opera – such was their puritanical conservatism – forbade her to accept an engagement to sing at Covent Garden Opera House. Annie had a will of her own,

Marconi (*studio portrait*)

however, and persuaded her father and mother to let her study singing in Italy by way of consolation. The Jameson whisky firm did their Italian business through a Bologna banker called de Renoli, who happened to be the father of Giuseppe Marconi's first wife; and whilst staying with the de Renoli family, Annie naturally met their widower son-in-law. The couple fell in love at once, and before long the young Irishwoman had settled down most happily in the well-to-do surroundings of prosperous northern Italy.

Thus it will be seen that Marconi inherited, among other things, a dour flair for commercial success from his father, and strong individualism and a deep musical background from his mother. Both were to hold him in good stead in the career he was to follow so effectively for the greater benefit of mankind.

Annie Marconi had one son, Alfonso, a year after her runaway wedding, but nine years were to elapse before she had another baby. He was born in the massive, heavily-shuttered Marescalchi Palace in the centre of Bologna, which his father had taken as a town house for the winter, and Guglielmo's first sight of day must have been the shafts of bright sunlight streaming in through the shutters into the lofty room from the walled garden at the rear. In the household rejoicing that followed his safe arrival, the Marconi servants crowded into their mistress's bedroom to offer their congratulations and get a glimpse of the new baby. With more excitement than tact an old gardener blurted out: *'Che orecchi grandi ha!'* – 'What big ears he has!' Family legend has it that his mother, weak as she was, flashed back in her Irish way: 'He will be able to hear the still, small voice of the air.' Certainly this was the physical feature most fitted to the man who was destined to extend so much the science of talking at a distance.

For Italy, the year of 1874 was not an easy one. There had lately been long and bitter patriotic struggles over the unification of the country, the capital, Rome, had only a few years before been freed from the control of the French, and the republican nationalist and guerrilla leader, Garibaldi, had just succeeded in entering the Italian Parliament, in spite of his opposition to the power of the Pope. Above all, the uniting of the battle-torn country was proving slow and difficult, owing to the great social and welfare differences between the north of the country and the impoverished, backward south. But little of this disturbed the peaceful, comfortable life of the household in which Marconi grew up. The Villa Grifone, at Pontecchio, was a handsome house set in a fine estate of chestnut trees, vineyards and rich fields, standing on a hill with mountains behind and a river below. It lay in the centre of the prosperous northern half of the country, so Marconi's boyhood was completely untroubled and free from difficulty.

In Britain, the great changes of the Industrial Revolution were not yet over, and progress at home continued steadily. Education had become compulsory, trade unions had been made legal, the franchise system improved. In the year 1874 Mr Gladstone, the Liberal, was succeeded as Prime Minister

27

by Benjamin Disraeli, the Conservative, and Queen Victoria, already thirteen years a retiring widow, had for the second time a first minister who flattered and understood her in place of one whom she detested.

Some idea of the way the world went at the time of Marconi's birth may be gleaned from the fact that on that very date Gladstone reviewed the latest Budget in a speech in Parliament, while Disraeli, with the notion of securing for Britain half-rights in the newly-opened Suez Canal already in his head, spoke on war rewards. President Grant, of the USA, made a speech vetoing inflation in that country. A surveying expedition was busy examining the proposed route between the two American continents for what eventually became the Panama Canal. The newspapers contained details of a new man-made foodstuff, said to take the place of butter and called 'oleo-margarine'.

Although he had an elder brother and a much older half-brother, Luigi, Marconi tended to be something of a solitary boy, overawed by his unbending father, confiding only in his mother, and for ever going off to amuse himself in some escapade or experiment. 'It seemed I was restless,' he said in later life. 'In any event, I was always in some scrape.' As he grew older, he became more and more self-sufficient, more absorbed in his own world of science, invention and study. He had very little regular schooling of the usual kind, and never attended a university. His mother used to teach him herself a good deal, particularly religious and musical matters, and she engaged private tutors for him also. One man, a local grammar-school teacher named Bollini, had the task of improving the boy's Italian which, oddly enough, was not good, for he spoke English as often as his father's native tongue. Each winter the Marconi family would move south to Florence or Leghorn, where the climate was milder, and Signora Marconi would arrange for the boy to receive tuition there also. Nothing was too good for her blue-eyed, fair-haired

28

younger son, and although at first she did not understand what he was trying to do, she was a constant encouragement to him in his various often absurd-seeming experiments, backing him up in the face of his father's stern disapproval. But she could be strict, too, insisting that Guglielmo should continue his lessons regularly during the long summer holiday periods, no matter where they were staying, and keep up his Bible study at all times. When he was young she would read him two chapters from the Bible every day, and later she expected him to continue the practice. He did, finding in a simple religious faith much comfort and support, even before he grew up.

Guglielmo disliked formal lessons, and usually chafed at discipline of any kind. He felt, with some justification, that he could learn more by reading, of which he was extremely fond. Fortunately the library at the Villa Grifone was a good one, well-stocked with books of many different kinds. At first, young Marconi became enthralled in the stirring tales of the old Greek heroes, with Achilles as his favourite, but in time he began to find a tremendous fascination in reading about men like Napoleon, Washington, Garibaldi, and Benjamin Franklin, and of the amazing scientific discoveries, chiefly in the field of electricity, of men like Michael Faraday and Thomas A. Edison. With his strong inborn imagination, it was easy for the lad to see not only the immediate excitement but the long-term results that came from being the first to make great discoveries in science.

His wide reading, plus his own inventive mind, early led him to the field of practical experiments, chiefly with what even as a young boy he would call 'my electricity'. His closest companion during these formative years was not another boy of his own age, but a girl cousin named Daisy Prescott. Not far from the Marconi home was a small spa, to which increasing numbers of people were going for health cures, among them a Mrs. Prescott, a sister of Signora Marconi. One of her four daughters was the devoted and vivacious Daisy, to whom Guglielmo took a special liking, allowing her to see his apparatus and work when he was too shy (or fearful) to show it to the grown-ups. From her we know a good deal of what the young inventor was like during his early years – and just how absorbed he was right from the beginning in matters scientific. 'He was never tired of trying to invent something, even when he was quite a little boy,' she tells us, 'and he used to come to his mother, saying, "Come, Mamma, and look at what I have made in the garden." He would lie on the sofa in a half-darkened room for hours on end in the summer reading. Then he would get up and go out and work at something. Always he was trying to invent something, and I remember when he was a lad of thirteen, his bringing me into a secluded part of the grounds to show me how he could distil spirits. "You see I have to keep the stuff boiling always, or it won't come right," he said seriously.' Not for nothing, it seems, was he descended on his mother's side from a whisky distilling family!

According to his own daughter, Degna, Marconi told her: 'I was always in hot water those summers,' and it was the twin crime of wasting both time and material things that so infuriated old Giuseppe Marconi. His impatience with his wayward son was not lessened when it came to his knowledge one summer's day, when the adults were away for a few days, that young Guglielmo had been seen by the villagers senselessly breaking crockery. The lad had been reading a life of Benjamin Franklin, borrowed from the Grifone library, and had actually rigged up a line of dinner-plates on a wire along the edge of the little stream where he often played. When he passed a high-tension electric current from one of his home-made batteries through the wires, the plates were flung off on to the stones below and smashed to smithereens. After that, old Marconi went round destroying every piece of his son's apparatus that he came across. So Guglielmo tended to be even more withdrawn and secretive, and it was only through the conspiracy of his ever-kind mother that he was able to continue.

Miss Prescott's account, written some years later, of her long holidays at the Villa Grifone in the company of this strange, determined lad, gives us an interesting idea of the sort of experiments he was conducting there, in spite of strong paternal opposition, when he was only just in his teens. 'During that time,' she says, 'he had no teaching on electrical subjects, and used only to read any book or paper he could get hold of. Yet nothing else occupied his thoughts. His chief idea was to invent, and he used to say to me: "If you could only know, Daisy, what a lot of ideas I have got in my head." I remember going to see my aunt [Marconi's mother] one afternoon, and finding Guglielmo sitting by himself with a huge pair of scissors, cutting some very thick-looking wire into pieces of about an inch-and-a-half long. His pretty fair hair was tossed, and his clear keen blue eyes were shining! Although outwardly calm, I saw he was deeply interested in his work. "Well, Guglielmo, what are you making now?" I asked. "Is this your new invention and what is it to be?" "You will see when it is finished," he answered quietly, and this was all I could get out of him. He never would talk about what he wanted to invent. He managed to cut a piece of soft flesh out of his finger with the treacherous pair of scissors, so he put it away in a box, and said he would get it stuck on bye and bye, as a chemist did not live far off.' In spite of accidents, Marconi was busy mastering on his own the principles of electrical wiring and the transmission of currents.

'About a year and six months after this we all went up to Grifone from the Baths of Lucca, where we had been passing a few weeks, and the morning after our arrival we found our way upstairs to the top of the house where Guglielmo's work-room was. I looked round. In every direction there were white jars and curious-looking pots full of water, etc. "Well, Guglielmo, there is nothing much to see here. What have you invented?" I asked. I have forgotten to mention two curious carved pieces of wood which I saw lying in the next room, covered with tin, and which Guglielmo called "reflectors". "Well, come and look here," said my cousin. "Do you see this needle?" On receiving my answer in the affirmative, he added: "Then look, I will put it on this table." He then took a small mariner's compass and put it at the opposite side of the room where the needle was lying, saying: "Now look, I will make that needle move without touching it." I looked well to see that there was no wire near the needle, or anything to connect it to the compass. Guglielmo then seated himself before an ordinary electric pear-shaped glass bulb (the ones we see daily) from which a blue light played. He touched the small globe, and in an instant both the needle and the compass began to move instantaneously. The other girls and I, who were in the room watching this simple but wonderful experiment, were all vastly surprised. At first I could not believe my eyes. I walked from the needle to the compass, and tried in vain to find a very fine wire (even as fine as a hair) in communication, but there was simply nothing. I thought Guglielmo was joking and in a moment we would hear a burst of laughter and see him thoroughly enjoying my stupidity, but nothing of the kind happened. He was in fact more than ordinarily serious and quiet, and seemed to be pondering over something. At last we were all convinced, and very much delighted. At lunch my enthusiasm knew no bounds, and we all wanted to know everything about the new invention, but though Guglielmo was always most kind in his answers, he was very modest and when I loaded him with praise he would answer: "Now, be quiet, you think too much of me." '

He had, in fact, produced a simple oscillator, and using two pieces of curved zinc (not tin, as Daisy thought) as reflectors, had managed to send wire-less impulses across the room. As time went on, he was able to improve his apparatus and project his waves over greater distances – first the full length of his 30-ft top floor laboratory, then into other rooms in the house, down to the ground floor and beyond into the garden. He managed to work a bell or buzzer by this means, so that there could be no doubt at all what was happening.

Fortunately Guglielmo had already mastered the one vital skill necessary in all early radio work: Samuel Morse's brilliant Code. One summer holiday at Leghorn the lad had become acquainted with a kindly old man, Nello Marchetti, had struck up a close friendship with him and spent many devoted hours reading aloud to him, since his eyesight was failing. In return, and perhaps sensing the boy's inborn leaning towards the new realm of electrical communication, Marchetti taught him Morse, for in earlier years he had been a telegraphist, in those days a decidedly uncommon occupation. No old man could have done more for the future of his own calling.

Although almost all the support and encouragement Marconi was later to receive in his epoch-making work came from outside his native land, two other Italians did play an important formative part in the inventor's early years. One was Professor Vincenzo Rosa, of the Liceo (College) Niccolini at Leghorn. Amazed at her young son's passion for things electrical, Annie Marconi arranged one winter when they were staying in that town for Guglielmo to receive a course of private lessons from this gifted teacher. The result, on the theoretical side of his particular branch of science, was invaluable, and Marconi always remembered and paid tribute to 'the clear and practical method with which Professor Rosa started me in the study of electro-physics'. The other was a figure of international renown, Professor Augusto Righi, of the University of Bologna, whom we have already seen as one of those professional minds keenly studying Hertzian waves and intrigued at their possibilities. In the autumn of 1893, when he was 19, Marconi attended one of Righi's series of lectures at the famous old university, where earlier students had included Dante, Petrarch, Copernicus, and Galvani. Again, this was through the influence of his mother, for the great man was a near neighbour at Pontecchio and she had a persuasive tongue.

Guglielmo never actually entered Bologna University as an undergraduate: he was merely allowed to attend some of Righi's lectures, both then and later, also to borrow volumes from its library, and eventually to set up some of his experiments in his teacher's laboratory there. Although Righi later realized the full importance of Marconi's work in his own field of study, at this time he was kind but not particularly encouraging. In fact, he discouraged the youngster from delving too deeply into the mysteries of these fascinating waves. It was important, first of all, to study the theory of the subject, he said. Hertzian waves were not exactly new; the scientific world had known about them for several years. There was no hurry. Short waves such as he had produced tended to fade away in the upper air. Maybe longer waves would be better. But there was no known method of creating electrical impulses powerful enough to project them any distance into space.

All this merely spurred young Marconi on to greater effort. As he himself put it years afterwards: 'It seemed to me that if the radiation could be increased, developed and controlled, it would be possible to signal across space for a considerable distance. My chief trouble was that the idea was so elementary, so simple in logic, that it seemed difficult to believe no one else had thought of putting it into practice. I argued there must be more mature scientists who had followed the same line of thought and arrived at almost similar conclusions. In fact, Oliver Lodge had, but he missed the correct answer by a fraction. From the first the idea was so real to me that I did not realize that to others the theory might appear quite fantastic.' To Guglielmo Marconi, with his intense powers of concentration, living more or less in a world of his own making, intent on his heart's desire, it all seemed so clear. But to

34

others it might seem less possible, even futile, a senseless waste of time, money and effort. In spite of Righi's indifference, the young experimenter was determined to be the first man to give the world a system of communication by electrical waves, and he saw only too well that if he did not seize his chances soon, other men, better equipped both in scientific training and in facilities for experiment, would step in first and claim the prize before him.

Already he had his so-called laboratory on the top floor of the Villa Grifone, where once silkworms had been kept by the thousand. He spent more and more time there, locked in and tinkering with his wires and reflectors and oscillators. His mother, alarmed at his lack of interest in food, set down his meals on trays outside the door. And when he was not actually experimenting, he was reading up the work and discoveries of others. That way, he knew he would succeed in his object.

But now he was getting older, and his experiments and equipment more elaborate and costly, Marconi knew the time was drawing near for a showdown with his obstinate old father, who for years had been angered by his son's footling behaviour and mad obsession with this toy men called electricity. He needed money as well as freedom to carry on his work. One day, when kept short of funds by impatient old Giuseppe, he had sold a pair of shoes to raise money to buy wire and materials for batteries. He lived modestly himself: every cent he was allowed went to subsidize his work.

Finally, in an agony of shyness and reserve, Guglielmo went to his father, told him he was now able to operate a bell in one part of the house by waves transmitted from another, and asked for support and money – especially money. The tough old man had not been a shrewd businessman and landowner all those years for nothing. He was ready to listen, even to talk. But he wanted proof that this thing would be a good financial risk for anyone who invested precious lire in it. So

35

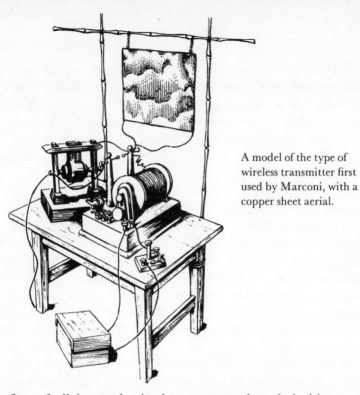

A model of the type of
wireless transmitter first
used by Marconi, with a
copper sheet aerial.

first of all he made the boy recount the whole history and
development of his invention, realizing wisely that his son was
still only at the threshold of the thing. Guglielmo pointed out
that he was now steadily increasing the range of his signals,
but the old man could not see any immediate prospect of
getting returns for any money he might invest. When there
was real progress to report he might be more interested. The
lad turned away in despair, but with an unusual twinkle in
his eye Giuseppe added: 'In the meantime, here is enough
money for the things you need in your work.' So the experiments could continue after all, and be expanded.

With our own after-knowledge we must not be too hard on
Marconi's father. In 1894 electricity itself still seemed only a
toy to a great many folk, while as for talking at a distance,
perhaps over hundreds or even thousands of miles, by means
of invisible electric waves, that was too absurd to contemplate.

36

Not only laymen were sceptical. As Marconi himself in later years told us: 'It was impossible in those days to foresee the eventual results of the attempts I was then making to evolve a method of communicating across space without the use of a material conductor, but even when I had only succeeded in sending and receiving signals across a few yards of space by means of Hertzian waves I had the vision of communication by this means over unlimited distances. To have made such claims at that time would have been to invite the ridicule of scientists, as, indeed, was proved when, five years later, I had the faith to believe that by means of the system I had evolved it would be possible to send and receive signals across the Atlantic Ocean.'

But now his vision and faith were enabled to persist, and young Guglielmo set about modifying and improving his apparatus. Heinrich Hertz had died at the beginning of 1894, and after reading an article by Professor Righi on his work, published in an Italian magazine, Guglielmo was more convinced than ever of the possibilities that lay before him. But with the inadequate equipment he was using, no real progress would ever be made.

To start with, the unreliable Branly coherer had to be redesigned. After much trial and error, Marconi found that fine nickel and silver filings, not zinc and silver, were best, and they gave improved results if they were placed in a narrow slit inside a vacuum. But after clinging together on receipt of an electrical impulse, it was still necessary to tap their glass tube to loosen them in readiness to receive the next signal. He eventually found the answer to that problem. 'To shake the metal filings automatically I inserted a lodestone (natural magnet) in the origin of the voltmeter circuit. This commanded a little clapper, placed where it could serve as a contact with the tube containing the filings. Every time I sent a train of electric waves, the clapper touched the tube and so restored the detector at once. . . .'

This meant that signal impulses could now be sent rapidly, without pauses between them. Immediately Guglielmo thought of the Morse Code. 'It was precisely at this moment,' he wrote later, 'that I thought for the first time of transmitting telegraphic signals and of substituting a Morse machine for the voltmeter. The extremely weak current available with my materials was insufficient to make a Morse machine function. I at once thought of reinforcing the current with a relay, and this I did later. For the present it seemed to me necessary above everything else to study the behaviour of electric waves at an increased distance outdoors, outside the limited space of my laboratory.'

At the transmitting end of his apparatus he used as an oscillator a rough adaptation of Righi's idea. This consisted of two pairs of spark balls, one connected to a long upright wire supported by a post and ending in a metal plate or cylinder. The other he connected to a metal plate sunk in the ground. This was not so very different from the machine used long before by Hertz, but it had much greater range, and eventually used much higher electrical power. At the receiving end of his equipment, for a resonator, he had his improved coherer and tapper, and before very long this was set to operate a Morse inker. So far his transmitter and receiver were basically the same as those already used by both Lodge, in England, and Popoff, in Russia. But now, and partly on advice he received from Professor Righi, he connected one end of his coherer to earth and the other to a long vertical wire similar to that attached to one of the spark balls. This was the first wireless receiving aerial. This way he was able to multiply many times the range of reception for the transmitting power he had available.

This discovery of the simultaneous use of two sets of earths and aerials, one of the latter for transmitting, the other for picking up the signals, was a major step forward and Marconi's first really original contribution to the science of radio. It was something that the experts had missed.

Although in fact wireless waves radiate from their transmitting point in ever-widening circles like the ripples so easily made on a calm pond, in those days men believed they moved in straight lines, avoiding obstacles if they were long enough. Marconi soon found that his range of communication increased rapidly if the height of his aerials above ground was increased. Again this was an important advance. But he also learnt that the greater the wave-length he used the greater the power he needed at his transmitting end to send it distances comparable with those giving successful results with shorter waves. At first it seemed that an impossible amount of power would be needed to send wireless signals any really worthwhile distance.

Already, by the summer of 1895, Guglielmo had so perfected his apparatus installed in the grounds of his home that, in his own words: 'I actually transmitted and received intelligible signals on the Morse receiver or inker.' Then came the improvements in the equipment: 'I considered increasing the dimensions of the transmitter in order to get waves longer than any that had been used up to that date – waves 30 or 40 metres long. With this in view, I replaced the two outside balls of the Righi oscillator with two slabs of sheet iron I got by breaking up an old tank. I did the same thing to the resonator. I found out then how to obtain waves at distances of hundreds of metres. By chance I held one of the metal slabs at a considerable height above the ground and set the other on the earth. With this arrangement the signals became so strong that they permitted me to increase the sending distance to a kilometre.

'That was when I first saw a great new way open before me. Not a triumph. Triumph was far distant. But I understood in that moment that I was on a good road. My invention had taken life.'

Further improvements, using the similar aerial and earth

39

connection at the receiving end gave results that even the cautious young 'ardent amateur of electricity', as he liked to call himself, described as 'impressive'. Before that momentous year of 1895 drew to a close, Marconi was sending wireless messages, still of course only in Morse, over distances of some two miles across the estate at Pontecchio.

Much help was now being given by the young sons of some of Marconi senior's estate workers, one of whom, given a few lira by Guglielmo for his services, thus became the world's first paid radio operator. Another admiring assistant at this stage was Alfonso, the inventor's elder brother. The huge joke of earlier days was gradually coming to be accepted as something of extraordinary interest. Before long, old Giuseppe himself would change his attitude and become an admirer of wireless.

One incident epitomizes those far-off but fateful days towards the end of 1895. Alfonso had been helping his brother by carting the receiving apparatus further and further away from the oscillator with its wave-producing spark, installed in the house and operated by Guglielmo. Among the gear that Alfonso and his helpers had to carry was a tall pole with a white handkerchief fastened to the top. When he received Guglielmo's signals at a distance he had to wave the pole so that the handkerchief could be seen back at the Villa Grifone.

But Marconi knew that eventually his signals would be communicating beyond the range of sight, and in any case to have real importance they would have to cross hills and mountains and valleys without interruption. One day Alfonso was told to set up the receiver on the far side of the hill behind the villa. It was a golden autumn day, with the vineyards heavy with black grapes, as Alfonso, aided by an estate farmer and carpenter, carried the bulky equipment over the hill and disappeared out of sight of the house. This time he carried a hunting rifle to tell Guglielmo if the experiment was working at this much greater range beyond the bulk of the hill.

40

'After some minutes,' Marconi described the day later, 'I started to send, manipulating the Morse key. . . . In the distance a shot echoed down the valley.'

It was a shot that was to change the history of the world, but no one was killed by it. It was aimed, significantly, into the air.

3
Radio Becomes
a Reality

Even old Giuseppe had to admit now that his son's invention
was likely to have some worth, but the Marconis were still
basically country folk, unversed in modern scientific matters,
and they were uncertain what to do next.

Partly to justify himself in the eyes of his father, partly to
ensure that his invention went ahead, Guglielmo wanted very
much to see some commercial use made of his method of long-
range signalling. The family consulted their local doctor and
priest, as Italians usually do when advice is required. Annie
Marconi, as usual, was full of enthusiasm. After all, she was
the only person, apart from Guglielmo himself, who had never
doubted that success would come. 'Being a loyal Italian subject,' he said, 'I considered it my duty to inform my government of my invention,' so accordingly a long and detailed
letter left the Villa Grifone for the Minister of Posts and
Telegraphs in Rome. After some delay, an official reply was
received. The Italian Government was not interested. Torn
politically, and rather backward scientifically, Italy could see
no useful purpose in the idea, especially when it was put up
out of the blue by an unknown young fellow of only twenty-
two.

Marconi was bitterly disappointed, and smarted under the
rebuff for years afterwards. However, both he and his mother
foresaw that the new system of communication would have as
its primary use the linking of ships at sea with shore bases, and

as England was then the greatest maritime country in the world, it was decided that he should take his invention there. 'Mind you,' he recounted afterwards, 'Italy did not say the invention was worthless, but wireless in those days seemed to hold promise for the sea, so off to England I went.' Italian lack of faith in the idea in fact drove that country's great inventor away, and robbed it of something that might easily have altered its subsequent history.

Signora Marconi consulted her Irish relatives, made all the necessary arrangements herself, and went with her son to London. He had been to England twice before as a boy, but this time he arrived, a slightly dandyish figure in Sherlock Holmes deer-stalker and long overcoat, ostensibly to see if the British Government would be interested in trying his form of signalling between lighthouses and lightships and the shore. Still he had not yet fully realized the enormous and universal importance for humanity which his idea was to develop in a few short years. Even less did he realize just how long he was to live outside his own country.

Amusingly enough, the Customs officials at the Channel port looked kindly on the Victorian-looking matron in her dark suit and veiled hat, and on her quiet son, but far less kindly on the two heavy trunks of equipment that accompanied them. In particular they were highly suspicious of his priceless, all-important 'black box', containing his transmitter. Perhaps this lean foreigner was an anarchist, or a spy? At any rate, they dismantled everything before letting it into the country, damaging some of the apparatus and being quite unable to re-assemble what they had taken to pieces. Once again, and not for the last time, Marconi was being handicapped by officialdom.

In London they settled in a house in the genteel district of Bayswater. Their first contact was a cousin of Guglielmo's, Henry Jameson Davis, a milling engineer with extensive Irish connections and a London office. It was now February 1896;

43

and under his guidance, in June 1896 Marconi registered in London the world's first patent for a system of telegraphy using Hertzian electro-magnetic waves, 'by which invention electrical actions or manifestations are transmitted through the air, earth or water by means of electric oscillations of high frequency'. It was British Patent No. 12039, and few who read it at the time could have dreamed of the repercussions it was destined to have on human history.

Meanwhile, Marconi set about improving his equipment in his strange new quarters and, as luck would have it, met through his cousin a man called Alan Campbell Swinton, who was already well known as an electrical engineer and researcher. Swinton was much impressed by what he had seen at 71 Hereford Road, Bayswater, and gave the young Italian a letter of introduction to Mr (later Sir) William Preece, then Chief of the Engineering Department of the General Post Office. As we have already seen, Preece was one of those much interested in wireless telegraphy, particularly as it affected postal and marine communications, and he had already made experiments of his own. In his note Swinton said 'from what he tells me he appears to have got considerably beyond what I believe other people have done in this line'. But the quiet, bearded engineer of sixty-three had achieved only a very limited success.

On the appointed day, Guglielmo presented himself and two capacious bags at Mr Preece's office at the GPO headquarters in St Martin's-Le-Grand. P.R.Mullis, then a boy assistant in that office, remembers that after mutual handshakings and the cleaning of his chief's gold-rimmed spectacles, 'the contents of these bags were placed on the table and seemed to consist of a number of brass knobs fitted to rods, a large spark coil and some odd terminals, but most fascinating of all, a large-sized tubular bottle from which extended two rods. . . . After one or two preliminary adjustments to the connections and brass balls by Mr Marconi, the telegraph key

44

was depressed and immediately the bell on the adjacent tube commenced and continued to ring. . . . I knew by the Chief's quiet manner and smile that something unusual had been effected. The following day and the rest of the week experiments were run off', many of them with Mullis as the Italian's assistant. He was much taken with the inventor's way of always courteously saying 'We will do this, or that . . .' never giving orders, or boasting.

Preece was very much impressed by Marconi's results, and at once extended him all the co-operation he could. He actually gave him the run of his own laboratory, and at once arranged for the inventor to give official demonstrations of the new telegraphy in Britain. Far from being jealous of the young man's success, he was very anxious to prove its worth to his superiors, and to get it properly developed. Always at the back of his kindly thoughts was the desire to ease the lot of sailors and lighthouse-keepers, to make their task safer.

Marconi's first demonstration was to send a radio signal from the roof of the GPO building in St Martin's-Le-Grand to other Government buildings nearby, among them the Savings Bank Department in Queen Victoria Street. The transmitter that had been clicking merrily away on a table in Hereford Road, Bayswater, worked perfectly in these tests, signals being sent and picked up for distances of over 300 yards.

Whilst Guglielmo was busy setting up his apparatus on the Post Office roof he happened to glance over the edge down to the street below and noticed a red-haired man standing there on the pavement watching him intently. 'What are you doing up there?' shouted the man. 'Come on up and I'll show you,' replied Marconi. In no time at all the man was up on the roof with Marconi: he began to help him at once, and worked closely with him for the rest of his life. He was George Stevens Kemp, an ex-naval petty officer who worked at the GPO on Preece's staff. From that day a close bond was to link the two men, and Kemp became the first of Marconi's devoted

45

little band of assistants who worked through all his great achievements in the years ahead.

By now the Marconi system of talking at a distance was becoming known in scientific circles, although as Guglielmo expected, there was much doubt and scepticism. Even the usually wise old Lord Kelvin, who had himself done such valuable research in this field, was scornful. 'Wireless is all very well,' he is quoted as saying at this time, 'but I'd rather send a message by a boy on a pony.'

Fortunately Preece took the opposite view. He felt the London tests were so successful that he asked Marconi to give much bigger demonstrations over greater distances on Salisbury Plain, not far from Stonehenge. Guglielmo happily set up his equipment in September 1896 on Three Mile Hill, in the presence of experts from the Army and the Navy, as well as from the GPO. He used substantially the same sets as he had used a year before at home, including the reflectors. For aerials he used 2-ft square copper plates suspended 25 ft from the ground, also much larger plates only 10 ft from the ground. He also rigged up aerial wires 90 ft long mounted on bamboo supports, and tried sheets of tinfoil as well. Transmission was a success over distances of $1\frac{3}{4}$ miles, and the onlookers returned to London much impressed.

But the significant thing is not the repetition on English soil of earlier results on the Grifone estate, but what Marconi told a friend afterwards: '*La calma della mia vita ebbe allora fine*' – 'The calm of my life ended then.' This was very true, for ever afterwards Guglielmo Marconi ceased to be the quiet, inwardly-absorbed and unknown young Italian experimenter working on his own. Overnight, almost, he became a famous figure, soon to be world-famous, for ever besieged with offers, suggestions, propositions and claims from both worthy and unscrupulous people, for ever working in the international limelight, a super-businessman grappling with politics, nationalism, greed and stupidity – as well as getting on with his own great

46

task in life. Many people wanted to cash in on the invention, to become his agent or business associate. Others, less unscrupulous, were equally time-wasting, like the woman who wrote to complain that his wireless waves made her feet tickle! Marconi refused or ignored all letters, including one from an Italian bank offering him 300,000 lire for the rights in his invention, for he was quite certain in his own mind of two things. One, that he was still only on the threshold of radio development, with a vast amount of work and trial ahead. Two, that in the end it would be worth infinitely more than anyone was sanely prepared to offer in 1896. On both counts he was very wise.

More disturbing were murmured accusations that he had produced nothing new, or that he had cribbed all his ideas from others. But, in truth, he had seized upon an idea already in existence, *and made it work.* He never claimed more for himself concerning his initial discoveries which changed the world in his own lifetime. With characteristic modesty and perception in later years he answered all such criticism: 'By the time I was twenty I was fairly well acquainted with the published results of the work of the most distinguished scientists who had occupied themselves with the subject of electric waves; men such as Hertz, Branly, Lodge, Righi ... and many others. With regard to Professor Righi, much criticism was levelled at me in the early days because in my first experiments I used a form of oscillator which had been devised by him and which itself was a modification of Hertz's oscillator. By availing myself of previous knowledge and working out theories already formulated I did nothing but follow in the footsteps of Howe (inventor of the sewing-machine), Watt, Edison, Stephenson and many other illustrious inventors. I doubt very much whether there has ever been a case of a useful invention in which all the theory, all the practical applications and all the apparatus were the work of one man.'

At the time, however, loyal old Preece answered for him.

47

In a lecture to the Royal Institution he said bluntly: 'It has been said that Mr Marconi has done nothing. He has not discovered any new rays; his transmitter is comparatively old; his receiver is based on Branly's coherer. Columbus did not invent the egg but he showed how to make it stand on its end, and Marconi has produced, from known means, a new electric eye more delicate than any known electrical instrument and a new system of telegraphy that will reach places hitherto inaccessible.'

So far it had been established that wireless waves travelled satisfactorily over land, even when hills or stone or brick buildings intervened. But what happened when they were sent out over water? Preece was most anxious to find out, so he got Marconi to experiment over the same stretch of sea where he himself had tried signalling by electro-magnetic induction earlier, between Lavernock Point, near Penarth, in South Wales, across the Bristol Channel to Flat Holm Island and beyond to Brean Down, in Somerset, a distance of over $8\frac{1}{2}$ miles in all. Earlier in 1897, Marconi had done further transmissions over Salisbury Plain, using aerials suspended from kites. He had stepped up his range to $4\frac{1}{2}$ miles, noticing as he did so that the slope or angle of the kite-supported aerial influenced the direction of the transmission. This was a very important discovery, and one of which he was soon to make much use for really long-distance wireless communication.

This time, however, the distance was nearly twice as great and was almost all sea. On 10–14 May and again on 18 May 1897 radio contact was established. Preece reported 'excellent signals have been transmitted . . . and we have by no means reached the limit'. Invited by Preece to watch the transmission from Lavernock being picked up in England was a German professor who had been working on wireless, Adolphus Slaby. Hearing the first signal come through, he recorded: 'It will be for me an ineffaceable recollection. Five of us stood around the apparatus in a wooden shed as a shelter from the gale, with

48

British Post Office officials with Marconi's early transmitting
apparatus at Lavernock, South Wales, 1897.

eyes and ears directed towards the instruments with an attention which was almost painful. The hoisting of the flag was the
signal that all was ready. Instantaneously we heard the first
tic-tac, tic-tac and saw the Morse instruments print the signals
which came to us silently and invisibly from the island rock
(Flat Holm), whose contour was scarcely visible to the naked
eye – came to us dancing on that unknown and mysterious
agent, the ether.' Flat Holm Island had been used as a half-
way point, and a few days later the full $8\frac{1}{2}$ miles from Wales
to England was bridged by radio.

Meanwhile, back in Italy, they had realized Marconi's
greatness, and were putting up a plaque on the wall at the

49

Villa Grifone. It read:

> Honour to the merit of
> GUGLIELMO MARCONI
> who in this house
> when still very young
> carried out his first
> experiments, and by
> his ingenuity and study
> invented the wireless
> telegraph in the year
> 1895, admired by Italy
> and Europe.

He was so much admired, in spite of earlier indifference, that the King of Italy waived his liability for military service, allowing him to stay on and work in England. Officially he was designated as a naval cadet in training, attached to the Italian Embassy in London. As he had no duties whatever to perform, Guglielmo sent his monthly pay to an Italian hospital in London.

This satisfied the young Italian's intense patriotism, which lasted all his life. His next step was to protect his invention commercially. With money contributed by Henry Jameson-Davis, several of his colleagues in the corn trade, and other friends, a private company was formed, and on 20 July 1897 was registered as The Wireless Telegraph and Signal Co Ltd, with offices at Jameson's address near the Tower of London. Marconi was to receive a cash payment of £15,000, plus 60,000 of the 100,000 fully-paid £1 shares which made up the firm's capital, all of which he immediately devoted to further experiment, living very humbly with his mother in Bayswater still. He devoted all his time and thoughts to his invention, and as the thing became more and more talked about, he was in ever-increasing demand for lectures (which he disliked giving), and for outdoor demonstrations (which he greatly enjoyed performing).

We have to remember at this time that Guglielmo was still a very young man, inexperienced in the ways of the world. He revealed in later life: 'The English believed at the start that they had to do with a young man of scant experience who could easily be dominated.' But they, and others too, were wrong. Guglielmo Marconi, son of Giuseppe Marconi, was a determined fellow, resolved to control his own work and reap the rewards he had justly earned. Those hopeful of exploiting his wireless for their own ends received a strong omen of what was in store when, shortly afterwards and chiefly on Giuseppe's insistence, the name of the new company was changed to Marconi's Wireless Telegraph Co Ltd, which still exists as a thriving concern with world-wide connections, though it is now known simply as The Marconi Company Ltd.

In the summer of Queen Victoria's Diamond Jubilee Year of 1897, Marconi was summoned back to Italy by that country's Government. The Italian Navy was very interested in this young man, not as an alleged cadet, but as the inventor of a new form of signalling. He returned as an honoured son, a little over a year after he had left the country for England, a shy unknown with all his future in a mysterious black box. There were audiences with King Umberto and Queen Margherita (which greatly gladdened the heart of his mother), with officials of the Italian Ministry of Marine, senators, deputies, admirals and the like. Then they moved northwards up the coast to the naval base at Spezia, where Guglielmo set up his equipment on two ships and on a land base. He realized at once that the tall masts and rigging of a ship are the natural site for wireless aerials, and on the cruiser *San Martino* he was able to fit his 'elevated conductors', or aerials, at a height of 115 ft, to match the 120 ft transmitting mast which had been erected on shore. The weather was bad, and they had trouble with atmospherics, soon to become the bane of radio operators everywhere, but good results were achieved up to the increased range of 12 miles. The Italian Navy decided to adopt

51

Marconi's system there and then, so becoming the world's first navy to use radio.

So far Marconi had only shown what could be done by experimental transmitters and receivers set up just for demonstration purposes. On his return to England that autumn he decided that the time had come to install a permanent wireless station, and in the November this was done on the Isle of Wight. At the extreme western end of this island are the tall chalk rocks jutting out into the sea known as The Needles, and it was in the grounds of The Needles Hotel, high on the cliffs above, that Marconi set up his installation. A mast 115 ft high was erected there, and at the other end of the planned link an aerial mast of similar size was set up in the grounds of Madeira House, on the mainland at Bournemouth, some 14½ miles away. Not only was direct communication established between the two points, and between the Needles station and ships at sea using Marconi's equipment, but for over four years regular messages were sent across by radio. When, in 1898, the mainland station was moved four miles from Bournemouth to the Haven Hotel at Sandbanks, on the edge of Poole, the range was increased to 18½ miles.

Throughout 1898 Marconi did a great deal of experimenting from these two stations, often using a steam tug at sea fitted with a 50-ft high mast, and he noticed that winds and bad weather had little marked effect upon wireless telegraphy. He demonstrated the now growing possibilities of radio communication to many eminent men at the Needles station, among them Lord Kelvin. This great scientist was now so convinced of the system's potential usefulness that he insisted on paying the usual GPO rate of 1s. for the telegram message he sent to Bournemouth, thus establishing a claim to have sent the world's first paid wireless telegram. But he did so not to create a record, merely to show official quarters that this new form of telegraphy had reached a stage of real utility, not just a novelty interest. With the formation of Marconi's work into

Metallic cylinder aerial used by Marconi at the Needles, Isle of Wight, for transmission to Bournemouth, $14\frac{1}{2}$ miles away, 1897.

a private company, the Post Office's support had had to be withdrawn, but Preece continued helpful and sympathetic, and fortunately Kemp rarely left his chief's side.

For the next couple of years Marconi steadily increased the transmission and satisfactory reception range of his apparatus, often in the face of many difficulties. The messages now being sent were very slow by modern standards, rarely more than about 12 words a minute, but they were accurate and reliable. The crackle and click-clack of instant Morse came to be heard over the ether from a gradually-widening variety of sources. But at least two major drawbacks greatly worried the inventor at this time: all messages were being sent out with identical power, so that anyone nearby who cared to build a simple coherer receiver could eavesdrop, which would hardly encourage the public to use wireless for private communications; and two transmitters working near one another would blot each other out. These were problems soon to be solved by

53

Guglielmo's intensely concentrated mind, and it is significant of him that at the time when his company with its now growing staff were officially engaged on increasing and testing ranges, he was grappling with these difficulties.

After more very successful tests on Salisbury Plain, a striking demonstration was given to the House of Commons, when the Speaker sent a message across the Thames to St Thomas's Hospital and received a reply. Then Kemp and another assistant pioneered radio's inestimable aid to safety at sea by reporting to Lloyd's the ships that passed between Rathlin Island, on the north coast of Ireland, and Ballycastle on the mainland. In bad weather vessels could not be seen by either the lighthouse on the island or a look-out station on shore. They had erected a 100-ft high aerial wire near the lighthouse and a 70-ft mast at Ballycastle, and in spite of swirling fog and the presence of high cliffs, this link was highly successful and greatly influenced the eventual world radio linkage of shipping with Lloyd's in London.

At this point Marconi saw that a striking and popular wireless link was needed to capture public fancy and convince the man in the street that this thing really worked and had many uses. Under the sponsorship of a Dublin newspaper, he decided to provide the world's first radioed sports report by covering the July yacht races of the Kingstown Regatta, a kind of Irish Cowes Week. On his hired steam tug, the *Flying Huntress*, he rigged up a 65-ft high aerial on the mast, while Kemp was ashore at Kingstown, receiving the messages through a mast soaring 120 ft above the harbour-master's house. Marconi was always deeply attached to the sea and loved yachting, so he had a grand time cruising up and down the Irish Channel reporting at close quarters such messages as: THE ALISA STAYED, AND WENT AWAY ON THE PORT TACK, AS DID ALSO THE ASTRID and THE RAINBOW HAVING CROSSED THE LINE BEFORE THE GUN WAS FIRED, WAS RECALLED, THEREBY LOSING THREE-AND-A-QUARTER MINUTES. Kemp rapidly transcribed the Morse from the inker at his end, phoning each message to the newspaper offices in Dublin, some 5 miles away. The paper's 'substantial payment' for this service was useful to Marconi's company, and the tremendous publicity received as a result, especially as messages had been sent over 35 miles at sea, was all he wished for. But one person who read the account of the Kingstown Regatta sports report can scarcely have been in the young Italian's thoughts, for she was Queen Victoria herself.

The Queen was determined to see this new wireless invention for herself, and it so happened that her son the Prince of Wales (later King Edward VII) had injured his knee in Paris and was convalescing in the Royal Yacht *Osborne*, moored off Cowes for the 1898 Regatta there. The Prince of Wales was doubtless unwilling to submit too much to his aged mother's worrying concern for his health (he was, after all, 57 years old!), so he had the Royal Yacht cruise around from time to time and moor out of sight of her favourite residence on the Isle of Wight, Osborne House. But he had not reckoned with Marconi's wireless for she invited its inventor to rig up his apparatus in her grounds and maintain regular communication with the Yacht. Marconi was pleased at this royal summons, both for itself and for the opportunity it offered him 'to study and meditate upon new and interesting elements concerning the influence of hills on wireless communication'.

At any rate, during that August some hundred and fifty messages were received from the Prince and his doctor aboard the *Osborne* and passed to the old Queen, some of them quite lengthy, others brief and reassuring, like: HRH THE PRINCE OF WALES HAS PASSED ANOTHER EXCELLENT NIGHT, AND THE KNEE IS IN GOOD CONDITION. It is said that whilst fixing his equipment in the grounds of Osborne House, Marconi saw the Queen walk by and greeted her, doffing his hat. The eccentric old lady was annoyed at what she considered an unjustified liberty from a stranger and so completely ignored

55

him. Marconi was so offended at this, and at being told by the gardener to 'go back and round' to avoid encountering Her Majesty at exercise, that he threatened to leave at once. On being told, Queen Victoria is supposed to have replied haughtily: 'Get another electrician', and a courtier had to explain to her that the Italian was no ordinary electrician and had no English counterpart. All ended happily, however, for she later gave Marconi an audience and wished him success in his work.

In March 1899 a further striking account of the work of the irreplaceable electrician appeared in the London technical journal, *The Electrician*: 'On Saturday last the first practical application of wireless telegraphy on the occasion of a shipwreck was made between the East Goodwin Lightship and the South Foreland Lighthouse. A German vessel, the *Elbe*, went ashore at the south of the Goodwin Sands, and the South Goodwin Lightship fired signals, a thick fog prevailing at the time. The signals being heard at the East Goodwin Lightship, communication through the wireless telegraph apparatus at that lightship was made with the lighthouse, from whence telegraphic messages were sent on to Kingsdown and Ramsgate for lifeboats to put out.' Shortly after this, the East Goodwin Lightship was itself run down and nearly cut in two by another ship in dense fog, and her wireless call to the shore for help undoubtedly saved the lives of her crew of seven by fetching out the Ramsgate Lifeboat to her aid. Soon there were other reports of life and property being saved at sea by the swift use of wireless, and no one was more gratified than Marconi himself. In early youth he had wanted to be a sailor, and like Preece he retained all his life a deep concern for the danger and the loneliness that men had to endure on ships and lighthouses. If his invention did nothing more than to alleviate that danger and that loneliness, as it was soon to do, he would have been more than content.

Meanwhile, in 1899, another sea link was ready to be

forged: the English Channel between England and France. Marconi equipment of the same type as had been used in all these tests bridged that gap by sending messages from Wimereux, near Boulogne, to the South Foreland, near Dover, a distance of some 32 miles. Marconi himself acted as the operator on the French side and initiated the 'great number of messages in French and English' that crossed and re-crossed the Channel on that historic day, 27 March 1899, by sending the agreed call-sign: vvv. Very soon his own receiver clicked out the response from South Foreland: vм (Your message perfect). Immediately he replied with the same enthusiasm that was soon to fire countless professional radio operators and amateur 'hams': SAME HERE. TWO CMS. (the length of the transmitting spark). vvv. It was V for Victory indeed. Later Marconi paid a nice tribute to the man whose filings coherer made reception possible by tapping out: MARCONI SENDS M. BRANLY HIS RESPECTFUL COMPLIMENTS ACROSS THE CHANNEL THIS FINE ACHIEVEMENT BEING PARTLY DUE TO THE REMARKABLE RESEARCHES OF M. BRANLY. Any tendency to take all this too seriously was dispelled two days afterwards by the American journalist Cleveland Moffett who radioed from Wimereux to his editor: MCCLURE, DOVER: GNITEERG MORF ECNARF OT DNALGNE HGUORHT EHT REHTE – MOFFETT. In a minute or two came the reply: MOFFETT, BOULOGNE: YOUR MESSAGE RECEIVED. IT READS ALL RIGHT. VIVA MARCONI – MCCLURE.

In writing a congratulatory letter to Marconi on this latest achievement, Preece said: 'I never had a doubt of it.' The man who received that letter from his old friend and supporter never had a doubt that the next wireless link would be over a much greater stretch of water, nothing less than the Atlantic Ocean itself.

4

Across the Atlantic

As the twentieth century dawned, Marconi was still busy ironing out the immediate difficulties in his wireless. He had seen his company start its first works, in a former furniture warehouse at Chelmsford, amid the usefully flat Essex countryside. There were made and tested the 10-inch induction coils and coherers that formed the main items of equipment in use at that time. He had seen the world's navies, led by Britain, France, Germany, and Italy, take up his system for their signalling, and he had seen commercial shipping companies, led by the German Nord-Deutscher-Lloyd line with their Atlantic liner *Kaiser Wilhelm der Grosse*, begin to fit his apparatus in their vessels, primarily for business and navigational messages. He had seen the formation of an offshoot of his company formed for this very purpose. Styled The Marconi International Marine Communication Co Ltd, it had to negotiate a maze of international laws relating to wireless communication at sea, since already the governments of many countries had secured official monopolies concerning radio telegraphy, at least where land stations on shore were involved. It hoped 'to establish marine wireless telegraphy on a sound commercial basis practically throughout the world', a praiseworthy aim, but one which was to take time.

Marconi had also taken out his second great patent, the famous 'Four Sevens Patent', No. 7777, of 1900, which introduced the device of tuning his apparatus, whereby the maximum power was transferred to the transmitting aerial, and from the receiving aerial, to the set. It was the answer to the difficulty of poor signalling efficiency, and the cancelling-out of stations working near one another. As with his original patent, the novelty consisted not in a new discovery of a scientific principle, but in the method of its application in a practical way. Selective tuning at both ends of his system was achieved by controlling the natural frequency of oscillation of a circuit from the spark used, and again it was a brilliant application of facts already long known. This system of tuned, or as Marconi called it, 'syntonized', transmission and reception, marked a major step forward in the history of radio.

He had seen wireless communication effected over some 65 miles, between Portland and Portsmouth, in tests carried out by the Royal Navy, and he had seen the first merchant ship equipped for the ordinary commercial operation of public wireless traffic, the Beaver Line's *Lake Champlain*, set sail from Liverpool en route for Montreal, and had watched with enormous satisfaction when she talked (in Morse) with the wireless-equipped Cunarder *Lucania* on the high seas.

And significantly, he had already been to America, intrigued by their lavish offers, and had faced their livewire publicity from the moment he arrived in the New World. There had been feelers for the purchase of the American patent rights in his invention, requests to give demonstrations to the US Navy, and a demand to give wireless reports of the America Cup yacht races to two New York newspapers. But before any of this could begin, American readers were given a forthright and amusing picture of the man as he disembarked from the Cunarder *Aurania*: 'Few of the many who were on the pier recognized in the youthful, almost boyish-looking man the bearer of a name that has become distinguished in electrical circles . . . a serious, somewhat self-centred young man who spoke little but then always to the point . . . no bigger than a Frenchman and not older than a quarter century. He is a

59

mere boy, with a boy's happy temperament and enthusiasm, and a man's nervous view of his life work. His manner is a little nervous and his eyes dreamy. He acts with the modesty of a man who merely shrugs his shoulders when accused of discovering a new continent. . . . When you meet Marconi you're bound to notice that he's a "for'ner". This information is written all over him. His suit of clothes is English. In stature he is French. His boot heels are Spanish military. His hair and moustache are German. His mother is Irish. His father is Italian. And altogether, there's little doubt that Marconi is a thorough cosmopolitan.' Behind the reporter's strident phrases lay a good deal of truth. On the return journey, on board the *St Paul*, Marconi set up his apparatus, and at a range of about 60 miles established contact with the station at the Needles and received the latest news, including some of events in the Boer War in South Africa. These items were immediately printed on board ship in the form of a news-sheet, the first ever to be published at sea containing news received by radio.

All in all, it was no mean achievement for a man of only twenty-seven. But far greater things beckoned him. Although he came from the Old World and the old century, Marconi had seen the New World, with all its vitality and promise, and he had seen his invention move steadily into the new century. He knew, instinctively, that if he could achieve a link by wireless between the Old World and the New, his discovery would go forward to a permanent, everyday place in human life, and the scoffers and the sceptics all over the globe would be silenced for ever. It would be his greatest test, yet he knew he would succeed.

With typically boyish enthusiasm, Marconi always referred to this project as 'the big thing', and in fact as early as July 1900 had decided on the best site for the English end of the operation. He always chose to work from lonely, bleak coasts, preferably with high cliffs, believing that the higher the natural elevation on which he built his stations, the better

G. Marconi (signature)

THE TRANSATLANTIC TIMES.

VOLUME I.   NUMBER I.

BULLETINS

THE TRANSATLANTIC TIMES

Published on board the "*ST PAUL*," at Sea, *en route* for England, November 15th, 1899.

One Dollar per Copy in aid of the Seamen's Fund.

Mr. W W Bradfield, Editor in - Chief. Mr T Bowden, As-i tant Editor. Miss J B Holman, Treasurer. Mr H H McClure, Managing Editor.

Through the courtesy of Mr G Marconi, the passengers on board the "St Paul," are accorded a rare privilege, that of receiving news several hours before landing. Mr Marconi and his assiftants have arranged for work the apparatus used in reporting the Yacht Race in New York, and are now receiving dispatches from their station at the Needles. War news from South Africa and home messages from London and Paris are being received,

The most important dispatches are published on the opposite page. As all know, this is the first time that such a venture as this has been undertaken. A Newspaper published at Sea with Wireless Telegraph messages received and printed on a ship going twenty knots an hour !

This is the 52nd voyage eastward of the "St Paul." There are 375 passengers on board, counting the distinguished and extinguished The days' runs have been as follows :—

Nov, 9th   435
,,   10th   436
,,   11th   425
,,   12th   424
,,   13th   431
,,   14th   414
,,   15th   412

97 miles to Needles at 12 o'clock, Nov, 15th.

1.50 p m . . . . . — . First Signal received, 66 miles from Needles.

2·40   "Was that you "St. Paul"? 50 miles from Needles.

2·50   Hurrah ! Welcome Home ! Where are you?

3·30   40 miles, Ladysmith, Kimberley and Mafeking holding out well.   No big battle. 15,000 men recently landed.

3·40.   "At. Ladysmith no more killed.   Bombardment at Kimberley effected the destruction of ONE TIN POT.   It was auctioned for £200 It is felt that period of anxiety and strain is over, and that our turn has come."

4.00   Sorry to say the U. S. A. Cruiser "Charleston " is lost. All hands saved

The thanks of the Editors are given to Captain Jamison, who grants us the privilege of this issue

'The Transatlantic Times', 1899, the first transatlantic newspaper.

would be the results, especially if no buildings or other obstructions intervened. The place chosen was Poldhu, on top of a 120-ft high granite cliff on the rocky Lizard area of South Cornwall facing the open Atlantic. Marconi persuaded the board of his company to find £50,000 to build a really high-powered transmitter here, at least a hundred times more powerful than anything used before, managing to convince his fellow directors that the idea was a sound one.

But if those who had invested money in Marconi's system were persuaded to finance this great new venture, most other people, scientific and non-scientific, were very sceptical. The trouble was that in 1901 it was generally believed that wireless waves emanated from a transmitter in straight lines, like the beam of a torch or searchlight. Thus, it was believed, when waves were sent out to distances beyond a hundred miles or so, the curvature of the earth would cause them to project straight out into space and be lost, just as a horizontal light

61

beam from a lighthouse is eventually 'lost', not continuing conveniently round the curving surface of the earth. Now the strange thing is that although he lacked all the intensive scientific training of the doubters, Marconi had an instinctive feeling that this belief was wrong. And when his station at Poldhu began experimental transmissions that were received successfully at St Catherine's Point, the southernmost tip of the Isle of Wight, a distance of 186 miles, and then at Crookhaven, 225 miles away on the west coast of Ireland, both with good strong, signals, he was confident that his 'hunch' would be proved correct. Over such distances as these the waves had acted just the same as they did over quite short distances, it seemed.

As the function of any wireless transmitting aerial is to radiate electrical energy over a distance, it needs to be as high as possible and the current in it should be as great as possible. Here were the two main essentials of the Poldhu station, as Marconi well knew, and his original plans there included a ring of 20 masts, 200 ft in diameter, surrounding the transmitter buildings, each mast to be 200 ft high, far taller than any aerial he had used before. There were to be some 400 wires arranged in the form of an inverted cone, designed to send out signals far more powerful than any the ether had so far known. Unfortunately, this grandiose erection was never proved, for in September 1901, when all was nearly ready, a great sea gale wrecked the lot, luckily without injury or damage to the buildings.

Time was vital to Marconi, for he wanted to span the Atlantic before the year was out, so he ordered the erection of a simpler form of aerial, consisting of 60 wires slung fanwise between two masts, which were only 170 ft high. Realizing that considerable power would be necessary if his signals were to carry 2,000 miles or so, he had built a most elaborate apparatus having a power of 20–25 kilowatts, then considered quite extraordinary. (A modern broadcasting station may

The fan aerial at Poldhu, Cornwall.

Marconi's transmitting apparatus at Poldhu, 1901, used for the first transatlantic message.

employ several hundred kilowatts power.) This involved trans-
forming the laboratory type of equipment – simple induction
coils, Leyden jar type condensers and the like – into a real
engineering plant.

No one had hitherto had any experience of high frequency
electrical engineering on such a scale, and with his usual
unerring flair for picking the right man to help him, Marconi
chose the one man who had considerable experience in the
nearest thing, high tension alternating currents on a large
scale. He was Professor J. A. (later Sir Ambrose) Fleming, of
University College, London, who had led the introduction of
electric lighting in Britain. Fleming was appointed scientific
adviser to the Marconi Company, and designed much of the
Poldhu equipment. That this choice was a brilliant one was
proved beyond all doubt a few years later when he invented
the thermionic radio valve. This was to be the one invention
other than those of Marconi himself that led to the world-
wide spread of radio and broadcasting.

Already, in the February, Marconi had again crossed the
Atlantic to see about setting up the receiving end of his 'big
thing'. Kemp and an engineer named Vyvyan accompanied
him, and they decided on Cape Cod, in Massachusetts, where
'a bare and extended arm' of the North American continent
curves out into the Atlantic, with no land between it and
Poldhu. It was decided to duplicate the original aerial system
at the Cornwall end, the pine masts being formed from local
timber. Vyvyan was left behind to supervise the building of
the installation, the others returning quickly to England, but
once more the weather struck. In October 1901, a few weeks
after the Poldhu disáster, the Cape Cod station was wiped out
by a terrific storm, one pine pole crashing through the roof
of a hut within a yard of where Vyvyan was standing.

Marconi was still undaunted, however, and ordered another
station to be set up at the port of St John's, in Newfoundland,
then a separate British colony and not a part of Canada.

Marconi with his assistants Kemp and Paget with their kite
equipment at Signal Hill, Newfoundland, 1901.

'After taking a look at the various sites which might prove
suitable,' wrote Marconi after he and his two assistants, Kemp
and Paget, had landed in the New World again, on 6 December 1901, 'I considered that the best one was to be found on
Signal Hill, a lofty eminence overlooking the port and forming
the natural bulwark which protects it from the fury of the
Atlantic gales.' They had been forced to abandon the original
idea of tall aerial masts on this side, and proposed instead to
trail an aerial wire from either kites or balloons.

In spite of the patents he had taken out, Marconi was by
now beginning to fear imitators, particularly in Germany. So
he wisely arrived in Newfoundland with as much secrecy as
possible, shipping his bulky aerial and receiving equipment
and unpacking it as much as possible out of the public eye.
This proved very wise, and when a newspaper reporter did
track them down, Marconi had ready a clever plan to disguise
what he was really doing: he cabled the North Atlantic ship-

65

ping lines to supply him with the position of their outbound ships fitted with wireless, so that he could perform distance tests with them at sea. It was a perfectly feasible story, and everyone believed it.

Marconi himself recounted what happened next: 'On Monday, 9 December, barely three days after my arrival, I began work on Signal Hill, together with my assistants. I had decided to try one of the balloons first, as a means of elevating the aerial, and by Wednesday we had inflated it and it made its first ascent in the morning. Its diameter was about fourteen feet, and it contained 1,000 cubic feet of hydrogen gas, quite sufficient to hold up the aerial which consisted of a wire weighing about ten pounds.' But the weather was atrocious on that exposed headland, and in trying to pull their balloon in, its rope broke and it was lost out to sea. In Paget's recollection, 'the gale snapped the heavy mooring rope like a piece of cotton, so Mr Marconi suggested that for his crucial test on the third day we should use kites, and on that morning we managed to fly a kite up to four hundred feet.' This was in fact the second kite, the first one sent up sharing the fate of the balloon.

Paget described the fateful little scene vividly: 'The kite flew over the stormy Atlantic, surged up and down in the gale tugging at its six-hundred-foot aerial wire. The icy rain lashed my face as I watched it anxiously. The wind howled around the building where in a small dark room furnished with a table, one chair and some packing-cases, Mr Kemp sat at the receiving set while Mr Marconi drank a cup of cocoa before taking his turn at listening for the signals which were being transmitted from Poldhu – at least we hoped so.' The men at the Poldhu station had been instructed by submarine cable on 9 December to start sending the agreed set of signals on the 11th. They were to transmit the Morse letter S (three dots) at a fixed speed every ten minutes between 3 p.m. and 7 p.m. GMT, with five-minute rests in alternation.

66

Marconi (left), watching his men struggling with their kite aerial in the gale at Signal Hill, December, 1901.

No one ever described the result better than Guglielmo Marconi himself, as that rickety canvas kite sailed precariously in the fierce gale over the Newfoundland cliffs: 'It was shortly after mid-day (local time) on 12 December 1901 that I placed a single ear-phone to my ear and started listening. The receiver on the table before me was very crude – a few coils and condensers and a coherer, no valves, no amplifier, not even a crystal. I was at last on the point of putting the correctness of all my beliefs to the test. The experiment had involved risking at least £50,000 to achieve a result which had been declared impossible by some of the principal mathematicians of the time. The chief question was whether wireless waves could be stopped by the curvature of the earth. All along I had been convinced that this was not so, but some eminent men held that the roundness of the earth would prevent communication over such a great distance as across the Atlantic. The first and final answer to that question came at 12.30.

'Suddenly . . . there sounded the sharp click of the "tapper" as it struck the coherer, showing me that something was coming, and I listened intently. Unmistakably, the three sharp clicks corresponding to three dots sounded in my ear; but I

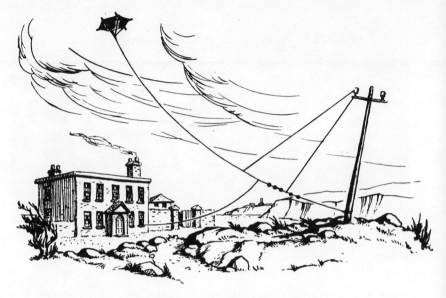

The kite aerial at Signal Hill, Newfoundland, December 1901.

would not be satisfied without corroboration. "Can you hear anything, Mr Kemp?" I said, handing the telephone to my assistant. Kemp heard the same thing as I . . . and I then knew that I had been absolutely right in my calculations. The electric waves which were being sent out from Poldhu had travelled the Atlantic, serenely ignoring the curvature of the earth which so many doubters considered would be a fatal obstacle, and they were now affecting my receiver in Newfoundland. I knew that the day on which I should be able to send full messages without wires or cables across the Atlantic was not far distant.

'The distance had been overcome and further development of the sending and receiving apparatus was all that was required. After a short while the signals stopped, evidently owing to changes in the capacity of the aerial which in turn were due to the varying heights of the kite. But again at 1.10 and 1.20 the three sharp little clicks were distinctly and unmistakably heard, about twenty-five times altogether. On Saturday a further attempt was made to obtain a repetition

68

of signals but owing to difficulties with the kite we had to give up the attempt. However, there was no further doubt possible that the experiment had succeeded, and that afternoon, 14 December, I sent a cablegram to Major Flood Page, managing director of the Marconi Company, informing him that the signals had been received, but that the weather made continuous tests extremely difficult. The same night I also gave the news to the Press at St John's, whence it was telegraphed to all parts of the world.' One private cable headed for Giuseppe Marconi at Pontecchio.

'The big thing' had come off. The greatest success had crowned the young inventor's years of toil. Those sharp little *pip-pip-pips* in his earphone before the first year of the twentieth century was out foretold the dawning of a whole vast new era of worldwide communication.

How had those signals transmitted from Poldhu been heard over 2,170 miles of ocean? The answer lay not so much in the apparatus Marconi used as in another phenomenon of nature not then understood, or even known. The receiver at Signal Hill was not basically very different from that Marconi had used back in 1895, but it did incorporate the latest type of coherer embodying the 'syntonic', or tuned circuits patented by him the previous year. It also included a special type of self-restoring mercury coherer, which required no tapping to loosen its minute filings, and in addition to the usual Morse paper tape recorder, they fitted up a telephone earpiece as an alternative method of reception. As it happened, the rough weather meant that the kite was constantly altering both its height and the angle of the aerial wire to the earth. The capacity of the dangling aerial was therefore constantly changing, which made it impossible to keep the 'syntonic' receiver circuit in tune, and for this epoch-making test the new idea was not used. Instead, Marconi decided on the earlier plain aerial-to-earth circuit, coupled to the coherer and earpiece in series. In this way, the beginning and the end of each train of high-frequency radio waves (they were long waves, wave-length rather below 2,000 metres) could be heard as distinct clicks in the earphone. This was an ingenious arrangement for it took advantage of the ability of the human ear to tell the difference between the actual signal clicks and the crackle of atmospherics, which the Morse recorder could not do. The transmitter at Poldhu, too, although it had much greater power, was still the same spark type.

The real ally Marconi had unwittingly discovered was the natural blanket, or layer of ionized (or electrified) particles of gas caused by the sun's radiation and enveloping the earth at a height of about 100 miles. We now know that there are several such successive layers out in space, and all have the property of reflecting, or bouncing back radio waves that strike them. These fall diagonally back to the earth, whence they are bounced upwards again to the atmospheric layer, or ionosphere, and the process continues around the earth until the radiating waves lose their power. Thus all radio waves travelling long distances reach them not by straight lines, which would indeed veer away from a spherical earth, but by a series of gigantic diagonal hops. In this way the waves can cover the earth and not be lost out in space, and it was thus that the waves carrying those first faint transatlantic signals in 1901 reached Newfoundland from Cornwall. Physicists and mathematicians at the time immediately set to work to find this answer to the phenomenon of Marconi's oceanic signals, and in 1902 a Briton, Oliver Heaviside, and an American, Dr A. E. Kennelly, working independently, proved that such a layer, now usually called the Heaviside Layer, did in fact exist. Later on, in 1925, the British scientist, Sir Edward Appleton, showed that other such layers also existed, both beneath and beyond it. All have an important bearing upon radio communications.

There was a certain irony in Marconi's excited sending of various cables announcing his great success that day in 1901.

Marconi at the Signal Hill station with the equipment used to receive the first transatlantic radio signals, December, 1901.

Although he was showered with praise and honour – the papers spoke of 'the most wonderful scientific development in modern times', and Thomas A. Edison himself reacted in astonishment to the feat of him he called 'the young man who had the monumental audacity to attempt and to succeed in jumping an electric wave clear across the Atlantic Ocean' – there were still scientific doubters who believed the Italian might be deceiving himself, and the world.

Worse than that, however, was the open hostility shown to Marconi by the cable companies. There were murmured accusations of trickery, talk of Marconi being deceived by 'the action of the ground current or lightning', which he mistook for signals. There were then no fewer than fourteen different cables on the bed of the Atlantic, and those whose money was invested in cabling were horrified at the thought that this young Italian's invention might speedily put them and all their costly systems out of business. At once, one company, the Anglo-American Telegraph Company, threatened him with legal action if he did not immediately cease the work he was engaged in at St John's, since they held telegraph rights covering Newfoundland territory. The Newfoundland Government and people were behind Marconi, having faith in his venture and liking his modest, direct manner and his concern for seafarers.

It was clear that Marconi could not continue working on Newfoundland soil without running into grave difficulties. Fortunately the Canadian Government stepped in and saved the day. Their Prime Minister, Sir Wilfrid Laurier, had been following the Italian's work very closely, and he authorized a grant of £16,000 for the erection of a wireless station on Canadian territory, plus enough money to pay for the completion of the work still to be done down at Cape Cod. It was too good an offer to miss, and Marconi gladly accepted, swiftly deciding on a cliff-hung headland site not very far round the coast at Glace Bay, Cape Breton Island, Nova Scotia. Work began there to build a really powerful and permanent station. The only significant stipulation the Canadians made was that the charge for wireless telegrams sent from Glace Bay was not to be higher than 10 cents a word, a highly competitive price for the cable companies to meet.

Marconi's next destination was New York, where he had to face more doubts, but noted the steady progress of the Marconi Wireless Telegraph Company of America, which was destined to be taken over by the United States Government in 1919. For the rest of his life, Marconi had to fight many battles against vested interests, those jealous of his successes or dubious of his claims, imitators and the like. Of this particular battle, with the cable men, he said only: 'The cost of laying cables is so large that the companies have to charge a high price for the service. My system will cheapen the cost very greatly.' Even without all the other advantages, this was a good defence of his wireless.

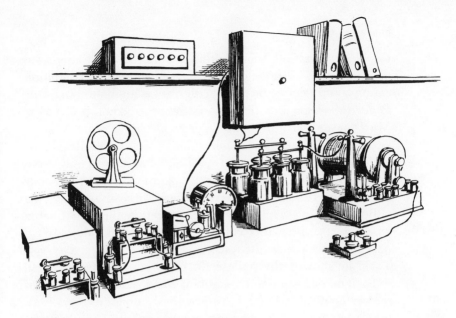

Wireless station on board the s.s. *Philadelphia*, 1902.

Then, after checking the work in progress at Cape Cod, he returned to England, and spent a little time with the mother who still believed in him utterly, but who saw little of him now. 'She's the only person on earth who understood my misgivings and trepidation when I left for Newfoundland,' he said. He was most anxious to give further transatlantic demonstrations which impartial people could confirm were actually succeeding, as well as to establish a west-to-east link.

So, within a month of returning to England, he tirelessly set sail again for Canada on the American liner *Philadelphia*. It was planned as a memorable trip, designed 'to blazon the truth of what wireless could do to a doubting world'. This time he had a staff of six with him. His intention was to test how far messages from Poldhu could be picked up and deciphered on board. He fixed a square wire aerial to the ship's 160-ft mast, and for the first time was able to use a tuned receiver, since the aerial remained in a fixed position, unlike the jerking Signal Hill kite. First, messages were received from

73

the Needles station, then Poldhu was tuned into. There was soon no doubt as to the distances over which radio communication could reliably be made with transatlantic shipping. The *Philadelphia*'s log recorded: 'Messages received on board from Marconi station at Poldhu (Cornwall) as follows: No. 1 – 250·2 miles; No. 2 – 464·5 miles; No. 3 – 1,032·3 miles; No. 4 – 1,163·5 miles; No. 5 – 1,551·5 miles. Signals 2,099 miles from Poldhu when we were in Latitude 42.01 N., and Longitude 47.23.' This time Marconi took the wise precaution of having either the ship's captain or chief officer in the signal cabin when the Morse clicks came through, and he also invited passengers to witness the tests. When the liner docked at New York, he showed the reporters a handful of Morse tapes all duly signed as genuine by Captain Mills, telling them: 'This merely confirms what I have previously done in Newfoundland. There is no longer any question about the ability of wireless telegraphy to transmit messages across the Atlantic.' The doubters were being silenced, now.

What Guglielmo did not tell the press was that a highly

The Poldhu Memorial.

important and interesting fact had been revealed to the little team by these tests. During the hours of darkness the maximum range of reception of readable messages with the coherer and Morse inker was 1,551 miles, while the simple letter S could be recorded over 2,000 miles. Yet in daylight no reception at all was possible beyond 700 miles with the power and wave-length Poldhu was using. This loss of signal strength by day, known as the 'daylight effect', was in fact another result of the existence of the ionosphere. During daylight some of the density of the electrified layer is unsuitable for reflecting back radio waves' which pass on through them and are lost, but with the coming of darkness, a change in the density occurs and some degree of reflection takes place. This explains why radio reception is always better after dark, but at the time the real reason for it was little understood, Marconi himself believing that bright sunlight acted 'as a kind of fog to powerful Hertzian waves'. With characteristic determination, he set out to improve the daytime range, finally deciding on the use of ever longer wavelengths. Not until some twenty years later did he himself discover that the correct answer to this particular problem is to use shorter and shorter waves.

However, Marconi's trial-and-error methods were always inspired by a deep, inborn faith in the new medium of human communication, and were always accompanied by a refusal to accept the impossible. Above all, they were infused with a deep and lasting sense of wonder – a wonder well described by Fleming in 1901: 'When it is realized,' he wrote in a letter to *The Times*, 'that these visible dots and dashes are the result of trains of intermingled electric waves rushing with the speed of light across the intervening miles, caught on one and the same short aerial wire and disentangled and sorted out automatically by the two machines into intelligible messages in different languages, the wonder of it all cannot but strike the mind.'

5

Radio
Grows Up

For the next twenty years and more, Marconi was a very busy
man, dividing his time and his long working hours between
his early station at Poole, Poldhu, his firm's works at Chelmsford, Glace Bay, America, Italy, and long experimental voy-
ages at sea. His work from now on can be divided into two
sections. First, and foremost, came the perfecting of transmitting and receiving apparatus, improving his gear, superseding
old devices with new, generally making radio work better in
every way. If it was through his efforts that radio came to be
born, it was also primarily through his work, much of it less
glamorous than in the past, that radio grew up so quickly.
Secondly, when he saw the reality of which he had dreamed
come about before he was middle-aged, he was able to delve
deeper and deeper into many other branches of the science,
to uncover new and exciting developments whose applications
we take very much for granted today.

In 1902, of course, he was not blind to the limitations of
long-distance wireless. He knew that a few Morse clicks, even
over two thousand miles of stormy ocean, could hardly be said
to link the New World with the Old in any lasting, commer-
cially-valuable sense.

So on returning to England once more he immediately set
to work on improving his equipment. The first in a long line
of technical advances concerned sensitivity of reception. He
now felt that if a printed tape record of a message was not

76

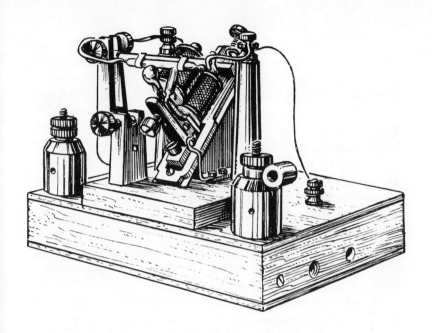

Early type of Marconi coherer receiver, 1902.

essential, better reception would result with an ordinary telephone earpiece instead of the coherer-inker set-up. The latter blindly recorded both the wanted signal and electric currents induced by interfering sources like atmospheric discharges, and so frequently confused the signal record. But the human ear could tell the difference in the two kinds of sound. Also, the coherer had always been the weakest link in the chain of radio reception, reacting badly to the rolling and pitching of a ship, and the vibrations of its engines. Marconi decided to replace it by his own 'magnetic detector', which he patented in June 1902 and the first of which, later described as a 'jewel of workmanship', he made himself at Poole with some very thin wire used for tying up flowers.

This instrument was based on the scientific fact, demonstrated by Rutherford in 1895, that when high-frequency electric currents are sent through a fine wire coil surrounding a core of soft iron, they have the power of varying the magnetic condition of the iron. Guglielmo fixed up a moving wire belt that passed beneath a pair of horseshoe magnets and was sensitive enough to pick up minute electrical impulses. It was a simple device, robustly constructed in a box shape, and quickly became the standard type of receiver, especially on board ship, for which it was particularly suited.

Once more the young inventor had shown his great gift for applying to a direct practical use existing knowledge that had been regarded as merely of scientific interest. Later, in 1906, the Marconi engineer C.S.Franklin, designed the 'multiple tuner' device that was always used with Marconi's magnetic detector. It made tuning-in to required wave-lengths simpler and more selective, and worked by tuning the aerial and the detector circuits simultaneously.

Of course, not all Marconi's work in the first decade of this century was an unqualified success. There were many snags to remove, many setbacks to face. There were even times when Guglielmo himself despaired of the future of his system and of the fortunes of the company that bore his name. At times he

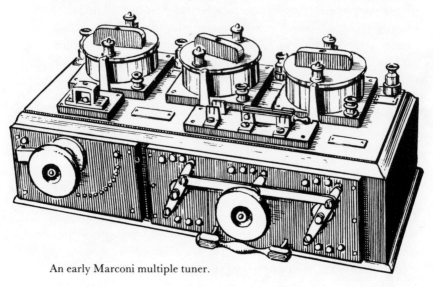

An early Marconi multiple tuner.

drove himself into ill-health through anxiety and over-work. In the summer of 1902, the Italian Government, now very anxious to support her still loyal subject, lent him the cruiser *Carlo Alberto*, with which to carry out a series of long-distance tests from Poldhu on a cruise that extended from Sweden to North Africa. Again the 'daylight effect' was most noticeable, 500 miles being about the maximum daylight range for signals. But when later in the year transmissions were tried from the now-completed station at Glace Bay back across to Poldhu, there were many failures. The Poldhu transmitter was too weak to send signals to Canada, and it was two or three weeks before any recognizable messages could be heard. Many changes had to be made in the aerial systems, many experiments made to improve the still very shaky link.

Part of the trouble lay in the simple fact that Marconi and his men possessed an incomplete knowledge of the properties of wireless waves, plus their continuing use of very crude and inefficient apparatus. As R. N. Vyvyan said long afterwards: 'An arrangement that gave good results one night the next gave very different results, and thus it became difficult to say for certain whether any improvement or progress was being made . . . we knew nothing then about the effect of the length of a wave transmitted governing the distance over which communication could be effected. We did not even have the means or instruments for measuring wave length, in fact we did not know accurately what wave length we were using.' The power employed at the transmitters was always too low for the results hoped for, and often atmospherics drowned the signals by their ceaseless crackle.

Marconi had long been aware of one grave fault of the whole system then in use. Although the available power was low, much of it was wasted at the transmitting end by being diffused in directions other than those in which it was hoped to send the message. Until greater concentration of the out-going radioed signals could be achieved, he knew that the distances covered would always be low in proportion to the electrical power used. So from 1902 onwards he worked long and hard to perfect a better transmitting aerial, patenting in 1905 his revolutionary 'horizontal directional aerial'. This gave much better reception when pointed correctly towards the receiving station, far better than the cone, or umbrella-shaped aerials then in use.

Most of Glace Bay's existing aerial system was scrapped in favour of the new design, a long horizontal wire system with a large capacity that was also far cheaper and easier to erect. Signals picked up at Poldhu were getting more reliable now, and to help meet rising costs Marconi made an agreement with the Cunard Steamship Company to supply their ships with a regular radio news service. What became known as 'Marconigrams' were supplied regularly from Cornwall to ships crossing the Atlantic, thus making possible the continuous production of the world's first ships' newspapers, now taken for granted by all liner passengers. But it was soon found that the site at Poldhu was far too restricted for the really big transatlantic link-ups, not just to shipping, that Marconi had in mind. In one plan he wanted horizontal transmitting aerials a mile long, and there was just not the land available there.

So, a little reluctantly, they looked around for a new site, and in 1906 began the construction of the first large-scale trans-oceanic wireless station at Clifden, in Connemara, on the west coast of Ireland. Poldhu continued to be a marine wireless station until 1922, being also the scene of much pioneer work later with short-wave transmissions and general aerial improvements. Finally, in 1937, the buildings were demolished and the site cleared as it was no longer required. But the historic spot of Cornish soil is marked today by a handsome granite obelisk, to commemorate for all time that the first link in Shakespeare's magic 'girdle round about the earth' was forged here, way back in 1902.

Another great step forward in Marconi's tireless dream of

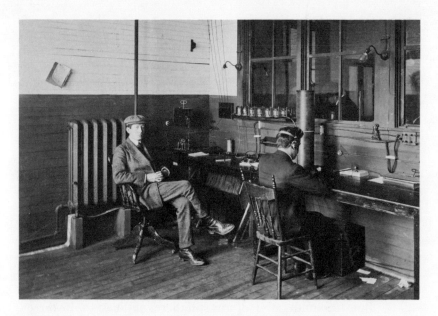

Marconi in the receiving room at the Glace Bay, Nova Scotia station in 1907, when the first commercial transatlantic wireless service commenced with Clifden in Ireland.

world radio came in October 1907 with the first trans-oceanic radio service, between Glace Bay and Clifden. Some 10,000 words of messages were transmitted successfully on the first day, at the cheap rates of 10 cents a word for private telegrams and 5 cents for Press ones. Improved landline connections at each end that linked London with Montreal greatly boosted this service, which was extended to the public on an unlimited basis in 1908, just four years after the first message had reached Poldhu from Glace Bay. Vyvyan commented later: 'Only those who worked with Marconi throughout these four years can realize the wonderful courage he showed under frequent disappointments, the extraordinary fertility of his mind in inventing new methods to displace others found faulty, and his willingness to work, often sixteen hours a day, at a time when any interesting experiment was being tested.'

Nevertheless, the public service was supported by a decidedly shaky technical background that would be laughed at today. Crude spark transmitters of some 50 kilowatts power operated on wave-lengths of several thousand metres, feeding receiving sets using simple magnetic detectors whose response to the signals they picked up depended entirely on the electrical energy they would extract from the incoming waves.

Still no one had thought of blowing-up, or amplifying, the signals received. And again, every improvement was directed towards using still longer and longer waves instead of shortening them. Waves 10,000 metres or more in length came into use, needing costly aerials, or 'antennae', as they were often called, sometimes suspended from towers or masts 1,000 ft tall. Even when transmitting powers were raised as high as 500 kilowatts, they failed to combat the infuriating jangle of atmospherics, often generated by tropical storms.

But the wonder of it all was still there, not least in the direct, uncomplicated mind of Guglielmo Marconi. On 23 January 1909 there occurred an incident that was once again to confirm in him how right he had been to persevere. In the darkness and the fog, off the Atlantic coast of America, the White Star liner *Republic* was accidentally rammed by the Italian ship *Florida*. The liner suffered severe damage, and drifted on helplessly, her sides torn open and her wireless cabin wrecked. Fortunately the young Marconi operator, John R. Binns, and his apparatus were unharmed, though only his emergency accumulators were working, the vessel's main power having failed. Binns found he had just enough power to signal the mainland: WE ARE SHIPWRECKED. STAND BY FOR CAPTAIN'S MESSAGE. By return, out of the Atlantic darkness, winging on the magic waves of the ether came the heartening response: ALL RIGHT O.M. (Old Man). WHERE ARE YOU? Binns wirelessed his position, and the shore station sent out an alarm to other ships nearby, some of which rescued those in danger.

Eventually the *Republic* went down, but over 1,700 people were saved, thanks largely to wireless. The world saw and

82

honoured a new kind of hero, the undaunted wireless operator. Soon the ranks of these gallant fellows were to be joined even more spectacularly by young Jack Phillips, the wireless operator of the ill-fated liner *Titanic*.

When this great liner hit an iceberg on the night of 14 April 1912 with 2,206 people on board, Phillips and his assistant, Harold Bride, stuck at their posts for hours trying to attract the attention of passing shipping, notably the liner *Carpathia*. The first message this vessel picked up said: COME AT ONCE, WE'VE STRUCK A BERG. IT'S CQD, O.M. CQD stood for COME QUICK, DANGER, in Morse the rather tricky — · — · / — — · — / — · ·, then just being replaced by the famous, now universal distress signal S.O.S., which is far easier to send · · · / — — — / · · · . On a suggestion from Bride, Phillips tapped out the new signal, the first time it had been broadcast in earnest. Although Phillips himself was one of the 1,503 souls who perished in the icy waters that ghastly night, he kept his wireless transmitting until the ship went down and undoubtedly did much to save the 703 people who were picked up by the *Carpathia*.

There was, nevertheless, some criticism at the time of what happened on that occasion, partly because confusion was caused by amateurs picking up some of the messages, jamming the then available wave-bands, while ships at sea were tuned in to other transmissions, and so missed the *Titanic's* S.O.S. calls.

If Marconi was profoundly thankful that over seven hundred persons had been saved by wireless, he knew that the others should not have died; and although he commented with relief: 'It is worthwhile having lived to make it possible for those people to be saved ... all those who have been working with me entertain a true feeling of gratitude that wireless telegraphy has again helped to save human lives,' he was quick to explain: 'Some ships failed to hear the *Titanic's* call for help because they were receiving news bulletins from

Cape Cod. With two operators, one could be working the news, the other – on any ship properly equipped – could be listening for distress signals, which would not interfere with the long-distance messages.' Even though the survivors marched *en masse* to honour him at his New York hotel, Marconi felt that his invention ought to have done more. He knew that too many ships had wireless apparatus too weakly powered, and that certain wave-lengths must be exclusively set aside for different kinds of messages.

A little earlier, in 1910, there had occurred another highly significant event in the history of wireless that was only in-directly connected with the sea. An American, one Hawley Hervey Crippen, known as Dr Crippen, had murdered his wife in London and fled to Canada on a liner. He was to be the first criminal to be arrested and brought to justice by means of wireless, for when the British police radioed the ship on which he was travelling, arrangements were quickly made to arrest him as he landed and return him to Britain. Crippen proved to be the first of a great many wrongdoers, both petty and great, to be caught with the aid of invisible waves that were already being called no longer Hertzian waves, but Marconi waves. If crime does not pay, it has paid far less since the police forces of the world have been equipped with radio.

At this time, the name of Marconi was being revered in every country in the world, and many people spoke of his genius. Yet with the modesty that never left him, he said to his young daughter: 'Do you hear them talking of genius? There is no such thing. Genius, if you like to call it that, is the gift of work continuously applied. That's all it is, as I have proved for myself.' And prove it he did, stepping up his range of reception to untold distances, notably with the messages he received at Buenos Aires from Clifden, a distance of some 6,000 miles.

It is important at this stage in the story of Marconi's work to realize just what had been achieved – and what was still

Huge synchronous disc spark transmitter at Caernarvon, 1914.

lacking. All the early Marconi wireless transmitters depended on the powerful spark they produced. Although any oscillating electrical circuit emits waves in this way, their radiation outwards is highly ineffective unless the dimensions of the aerial circuit match the size of the wave-length used. Thus ever longer wave-lengths required taller aerial masts and longer aerial wires. Furthermore, this spark transmission tended to be both wasteful of electric power and generally troublesome; since the waves emitted were not clearly confined to fixed wave-lengths there was constant difficulty with overlapping and interference. It also interfered with other transmitters that happened to be nearby; and as radio grew and became more widespread, this was an ever-increasing nuisance.

All the same, spark sets continued to be used for some time

yet – giving ships' wireless operators the nickname of 'Sparks' which many still answer to – and as late as 1919 there were in operation gigantic and cumbersome spark transmitters on shore used to send messages to ships at sea. They required vast high-frequency transformers to generate sparks powerful enough to reach out through their oscillating waves over thousands of miles of ocean. Spark transmitters actually sent out very wide bands of waves, which reduced the possibilities of careful 'tuning'.

A good analogy here is ordinary lightning, which is really an enormous natural spark transmitting on a wave-band so wide that it is heard as a sharp crackling noise on any radio set, no matter to what station or programme it is tuned. Normally, of course, a set will receive a broadcast only if its aerial circuit is adjusted, or tuned, to the same frequency, or wave-length, as that of the transmitting aerial. There must always be this 'sympathy' between both ends of any radio link, a sympathy nowadays brought to a perfection unknown when Marconi did most of his experiments.

Wave-lengths, by the way, are measured as the distance between the crest of one wave and the next, and may vary from 1 centimetre to more than 20,000 metres, and the various kinds of electro-magnetic waves (which include X-rays, ultra-violet rays and those producing heat and light) differ only in their various wave-lengths.

The wireless waves sent out by a spark transmitter were not produced continuously: they emerged from the transmitting aerial intermittently as the operator depressed the Morse key, breaking off when he released the pressure of his finger. Thus it was possible to send Morse so easily in a series of short or long bursts of wave signals. Such disconnected wave signals could never be used for anything but the dots and dashes they transmitted so readily: they could never be used to broadcast continuous sounds like speech or music.

Marconi had long been conscious of this, and in 1912 he

made another step forward by bringing out what he called the 'timed spark' system of transmitting, by which semi-continuous trains of waves were radiated into the ether, but progress towards the continuous waves used universally today was slow.

Two other important adaptations to wireless equipment had already arrived, even though their impact was also slow. Quite early in the century it was discovered that certain hard crystals, especially of galena (sulphide of lead), have the peculiar property of allowing electric currents to flow through them in one direction more easily than another. This led to their use as wireless detectors that can be relied upon to produce a series of intermittent signals less liable to outside electrical discharges than were the old coherers. These became in time the famous 'crystal set' receivers that so many people used in their homes during the early nineteen-twenties.

Even more important was the discovery (in 1904) by Fleming of the two-electrode, or diode, 'thermionic valve', which in time was completely to revolutionize radio. He had previously discovered that the heated filament of an ordinary electric lamp gave off a constant stream of electrons, or negative charges of electricity. A simple adaptation of this principle, using a vacuum, acts like the crystal detector in allowing the current to pass in one direction only. At first, this valve was used only as a simple detector, but when it was improved almost immediately by the American Dr Lee de Forest, who added another electrode which he called the 'grid', its real usefulness was ensured. But not immediately recognized, since for some years the thermionic valve was regarded only as an alternative detector to the magnetic or crystal types and nothing more. Gradually, however, it was realized that this glass valve could be used to ensure the generation of continuous waves at the transmitter, and also to amplify weak currents coming in at the receiving end – both far-reaching developments that were eventually to make the valve the

87

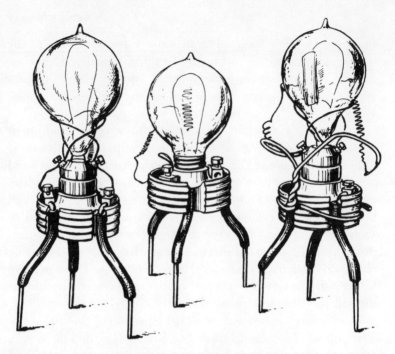

Sir Ambrose Fleming's original two-electrode valves, 1904.

most important single component of any modern radio apparatus. In various forms, and with additional electrodes, it has become the basis of both transmitting and receiving sets, and of television and radar.

It took World War I to bring about the next major developments in radio history, to achieve the twin discoveries that made Marconi's boyish dream a reality in his own lifetime.

In 1915, two American companies collaborated in the building of a transmitter in which hundreds of thermionic valves were used. These produced continuous waves, making the transmission of speech possible from a place called Arlington, near Washington, to Paris, a distance of 3,500 miles. A wave-length of 6,000 metres was used, and by this single feat was opened up the enormous, then still untapped possibilities of both broadcasting and radio-telephony.

The other discovery was Marconi's own and took place the following year. World War I was the first war in history to be fought with the aid of wireless in full use by both sides. Although Marconi, the loyal patriot, joined the Italian Army as a major and soon took charge of his country's entire wireless telegraph system, the impact of radio upon the conflict was itself twofold. There was the vast, unexpected application of wireless to the struggle by both sides on all fronts, on land, sea and in the air. And growing out of that application, in fact springing from the need to find some method of both naval and army signalling in Italy that could not be detected at a distance by the enemy, came the impetus that led Marconi to study seriously the use of very short radio waves for the first time. He found that they worked far better than the very long waves on which for years he and all other workers had pinned their faith. Before long he was able to perfect their use.

By the time of the outbreak of the war in 1914, the continuous spark method of transmission was fairly general, and very early on in the hostilities, it became clear to both the Allied and the German military leaders that so great were the possibilities of wireless in fighting the war, that their existing resources were totally inadequate, and must be immediately stepped up. Thus there came about not only an enormous increase in the apparatus in daily use, and of the training of men to operate it, but inevitably there also developed a great many technical improvements. The stark necessities of war gave radio a tremendous boost. Fortunately mankind was to profit by them when peace returned once more.

Only the navies were more or less prepared for waging war with the aid of wireless, though by no means all ships were fitted with radio as early as 1914. Army commanders on both sides viewed the invention as only a very limited and unimportant adjunct to visual or land-line signalling. As for radio in the air, this, like aerial warfare itself, was still completely untried.

89

Early type of direction-finding aerial on a ship, 1914.

It is an interesting fact that the first act of war was the sending of a wireless message. The British Grand Fleet had been holding a big naval review off Spithead at the end of July 1914, and was just about to disperse when a wireless signal at 5 a.m. on 30 July from the Admiralty in Whitehall diverted every ship to its war station. Then, when the British ultimatum to Germany expired at 11 p.m. on the night of 3–4 August, the Fleet under Admiral Jellicoe received the radioed message: COMMENCE HOSTILITIES AGAINST GERMANY.

Marconi himself supported the Allies, as did his country after 1915, and he must have been greatly heartened and impressed by the fact that before very long great quantities of Marconi apparatus, or at least Marconi-inspired apparatus, were playing a totally new role in the conflict. Not the least in importance, and dearest to Guglielmo's own heart, was the construction by his company of wireless direction-finding stations in Britain and many other parts of the world, by means of which watch was kept continuously on the movements of the German High Seas Fleet, submarines and Zeppelin airships. Although army units soon came to be equipped with low-power equipment for speedy land signalling and artillery range-finding, a completely new aspect of the power of wireless lay in their crude but not ineffective tracking apparatus to give warning of the approach of Zeppelins over England.

But of course the greatest advances were made in the air. The development of airborne wireless, without which modern civil aviation and the immense importance of aircraft in World War II could never have taken place, received enormous impetus under the stimulus of war. The first wireless message to be received on the ground from a plane was that sent on one of Marconi's spark transmitters by a Canadian named McCurdy from a Curtiss biplane at Long Island, USA, in 1910, at a range of one mile and a height of 600 ft. His feat proved that air-to-ground communication was possible. At first, the chief wartime use was from small aircraft

Early aircraft radio equipment, 1920.

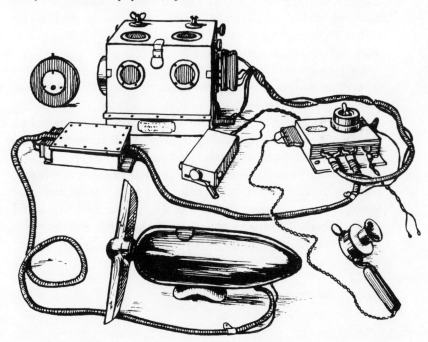

spotting for ground artillery, but with the growth of the Royal Flying Corps and the development of bombing raids and dog-fights, inter-plane telephony became urgently necessary. Small sets to achieve this, and the use of soundproof flying-helmets incorporating earphones, were finally perfected in 1917. Another landmark in radio history had arrived, almost unnoticed in the urgencies of war.

Not only was a wireless message the first open act of the war. Appropriately – and significantly, too – one was likewise to be the last. At 5.40 a.m. on 11 November 1918, Marshal Foch sent out from the Eiffel Tower in Paris the long-awaited message to the Allied Commanders-in-Chief that all hostilities were to cease at 11 a.m. on that day. This vital signal was intercepted by hundreds of radio operators in Europe, including the Marconi operator on duty at that hour at Marconi House, in London. There, men like him had maintained an endless wireless watch for over four years, linked with a nationwide network. In yet another quite new aspect of modern warfare, they had picked up over 80 million words of German radio propaganda, news, commercial and secret coded messages, which they reported at once to the various war and service departments.

But even more interestingly, this selfsame message was picked up out of the buzzing ether by Guglielmo Marconi himself. Sitting tense-faced and concentrated in his large, top-floor radio room in the big white Villa Sforza Cesarini on the Gianicola – the Janiculum Hill of Ancient Rome – earphones on his head as usual, he heard the fateful words in Morse from France. It must have been a moment of strange, profoundly thoughtful emotion for the man whose long-confessed and most ardent desire was always that this wonderful new method of human communication, which had been his life's work, should forward the interests of peace among nations.

6

The Era of
Broadcasting

In some ways it is strange that the demands of World War I
upon the Italians should have led Marconi to see the untapped
possibility that very short wireless waves might offer greater
advantages than the very long ones then in universal use. Yet
it is a fact. In 1916 and 1917 he investigated these short
waves very thoroughly, making experiments in the 2–3 metre
range, and developing for the purpose a small compressed air
spark transmitter which proved reliable enough to send messages over distances of a few miles. He saw that by using such
waves the chances of unwanted interception by the enemy
were much reduced, and also that shorter waves meant smaller
transmitting aerials, which in turn could be more easily used
with directional reflectors.

After the war was over, Guglielmo still pursued these possibilities, transferring his activities back to England and enlist-
ing the help of his old and trusted engineer, C.S.Franklin,
who was the first to notice the great increase of range that
short waves offered if the transmitters and receivers were
raised high above the ground.

By 1918 the radio companies of the world, including
Marconi's own, had put most of their money into the development of very high power spark transmitters for very long waves.
They had long assumed that wireless waves below 200 metres
in length were useless for serious global communication, and
by international agreement such wave-lengths had been offi-

cially allocated to the large body of amateur radio enthusiasts which had by now grown up, it being thought that there they could play around with their little transmitters and cause the least interference with commercial traffic. Such a belief was soon to be proved wrong, and the whole of radio communication revolutionized – thanks to Marconi's wartime idea, and his subsequent development of it.

In fact, Marconi devoted the next few years to perfecting short-wave radio, following his hunch against much scepticism and in the face of many snags. But first of all he needed one adjunct to the long and careful experiments on a world-wide scale he knew would be necessary. That this was also a youthful ambition of his only made him all the more anxious to acquire it. This was his own ocean-going yacht. His choice fell on a trim steam yacht, 200 feet long, of 730 tons displacement, with a high prow and a tall single funnel. She was not new, having been built in Scotland for the Archduchess Maria Theresa of Austria and later used as a wartime minesweeper in the Royal Navy. In 1920 he bought her, re-christened her *Elettra*, engaged a former Italian naval officer, Captain Lauro, as her skipper, in charge of a picked crew of 31, and fitted her out as a floating radio laboratory. 'The yacht,' he claimed at the time, 'not only makes me independent but it takes me away from curious eyes and distractions. I can work there at all hours of the day and night, finding without delay suitable grounds for all kinds of experiments which would be difficult and complicated to carry out on land.' A great many of his subsequent short-wave experiments were carried out from the S.Y. *Elettra*, and indeed she saw much of the remainder of Marconi's life work. The Italian poet Gabriele D'Annunzio called the sleek, white-painted, far-ranging vessel 'the shining ship that works miracles, penetrating the silences of the air'. (She subsequently had an eventful history, being seized by the Germans in World War II, converted by them into a modern gunboat, and sunk by an Allied torpedo off the Dalmatian

94

The *Elettra*.

coast in 1944. After the war, under an agreement between the Italian and Yugoslav Governments, she was raised from the sea-bed, towed to Trieste, and there made shipshape again, with the intention that she should be preserved on an artificial lake in a suburb of Rome as a permanent memorial to Marconi's work.)

Franklin had already used an extremely short wave of 15 metres for a directive telephone beam link between London and Birmingham, following Marconi's own Italian experiments. Marconi was encouraged to tell a gathering of American electrical engineers in New York one day in 1922: 'I feel . . . that the study of short electric waves, although sadly neglected all through the history of wireless, is still likely to develop in many unexpected directions, and open up new fields of profitable research.' This prophecy was a wise one; and Marconi's mention of 'profitable research' was soon to meet the need for a world-linking radio system that would really be far cheaper than sending cables.

95

In the spring of 1923 the *Elettra* sailed for the Cape Verde islands in the South Atlantic, with the inventor on board listening every day for signals transmitted on 97 metres from a special reflecting beam aerial set up at Poldhu. The reception was extremely good; though it ceased at a range of 1,400 miles in daylight, it extended much farther during darkness. Soon, Guglielmo was able to write home: 'The results have been truly remarkable, and well worth the time and money devoted to them. We can now do distances of 2,500 miles with one-tenth of the power required before, besides being able to send messages in one direction only.' It was certainly something to write home about, particularly as he noticed that although there was this usual disappearance of the longest range signals in daylight, they lasted for a time after sunrise at Poldhu and became audible again before darkness had set in at the Cape Verde Islands. This made him suspect that some new phenomenon existed in the short-wave band. He returned to England, and planned extensive further tests for the following year. In 1924 the yacht cruised through the Mediterranean towards Syria, and in Beirut harbour he was astounded to see that signals on the new, very short 32-metre band from Poldhu, 2,400 miles away, did not vanish by day, and were in fact as good as the night-time ones. Yet on 92 metres, with the same transmitting power, they behaved as they had done at the Cape Verde Islands.

What he was observing in practical fashion was the highly efficient transmission of short waves by reflection from that ionized layer in the upper atmosphere later to be termed the F_2 layer, though as usual with him, his work was years ahead of scientific theory. Marconi returned at once to England, and sent notification of his planned radio transmissions on 32 metres to Argentina, Australia, Brazil, Canada, and the United States, and at the appointed times the signals from Poldhu, transmitted on a power of only 1 kilowatt, were clearly heard in all these countries. Some, in fact, were clearer

Marconi in the radio cabin of the *Elettra*.

than the old long-wave transmissions sent out from the gigantic spark transmitter at Caernarvon. In far-off Australia they reported successful reception for $23\frac{1}{2}$ hours out of the 24. Almost at once, long-wave radio transmission on a world basis was rendered obsolete, yet it was to take several further years of close investigation and patient observation by teams of trained scientists before the natural mechanism by which these results were achieved was laid bare, and the complex laws governing the deflection of radio waves from the ionized layers back to earth were discovered. As had happened thirty years before, Marconi, the practical inventor, had outstripped scientific discovery and produced practical results.

At first, the significance of all this was not fully appreciated outside his own organization, but true to his hereditary business sense, Guglielmo pressed on with the commercial application of his work. In 1924 his company signed a contract with the British Government by which they set up short-wave communication between England and all parts of the

Commonwealth at speeds (up to 100 words a minute) that no long-wave transmitter or cable had ever achieved. With the so-called daylight wave, Marconi achieved his second great discovery, not only rendering obsolete his own long-wave transmitters but reducing the cable systems – finally – to the status of a secondary means of communication.

Before long, the value of the new system, using directional beam aerials for the transmitting of waves in the chosen direction, not at random in all directions as before, became generally recognized. Short-wave beam stations for commercial and general international use began to be set up all over the world, and in a few years there had developed the vast worldwide network that was far superior in every way to the wildest dreams of Marconi and his early associates, and which, with extended technical improvements, makes the world seem such a small place today.

Guglielmo continued to spend about six months of each year on the *Elettra*, and although he tended to visit England less often in the last years of his life, he still worked hard and long at his second great discovery, the enormous possibilities of short waves. There is no doubt he was exceptionally fascinated by the scope these ultra-short radio waves offered, and using the valve-oscillator system, he found that if a curved, parabolic reflector of moderate size was used behind the transmitting aerial, waves of only half a metre gave useful ranges of communication at very low power. In Italy, in 1932, he experimented with waves 57 centimetres long, using novel reflectors.

Always he was anxious to break down what barriers remained in radio communication. 'It is dangerous to put limits on wireless,' he said; and we know today just how right he was. In that year he was proud to be allowed to install a very short-wave radio telephone system between the Vatican in Rome and the Pope's summer residence at Castel Gandolfo, outside the city, and at a big ceremony that inaugurated the 15-mile

Marconi with
ultra-short wave
experimental aerial,
Italy, 1932.

link on the 60-centimetre wave, Pope Pius XI spoke to con-
gratulate Marconi on 'the continuous success that Divine
Providence and Divine Goodness have reserved for your researches and applications in this field'. The inventor, greatly
moved by this honour, replied: 'This first application of
microwaves fills my heart both as an Italian and a scientist
with pride and hope for the future. May my modest work
contribute to the achievement of true Christian peace throughout the world.' This link with ultra-short waves was the first
in the world, but in a few years its range had been successfully
extended to thousands of miles.

Speaking about the same time to a gathering at the Royal
Institution, in London, Marconi told his hearers: 'The general
belief is that with electro-magnetic waves under one metre in
length, usually referred to as quasi-optical, communication is
possible only when the transmitter and receiver are within
visual range of each other. . . . Long experience has, however,

taught me not always to believe in the limitation indicated by
purely theoretical considerations, or even by calculations . . .
I believe, in spite of adverse forecasts, in trying out new lines
of research, however unpromising they may seem at first
sight.' It was the old story of the venturesome amateur convinced of his own powers in the face of scientific scepticism.
In those words lay the whole secret of Marconi's life and work.

Universally recognized, now, as both the father and the
inspiration of modern radio, showered with honours by his
own country and many others, welcomed everywhere, finan-
cially independent, able to work just where he chose, free to
experiment to his heart's content and daily witnessing the
immense benefits his work had bestowed upon mankind,
Guglielmo Marconi might seem to have been at the peak of his
career. But he was over sixty now, physically and mentally
worn by a lifetime of struggle and endeavour, and his health

was failing. He had suffered several minor heart attacks, but his interest in his work was undiminished. Very late in his life he told a colleague, Luigi Solari, that there was still much to be learned about wireless, and he was preparing to learn it.

Although much of his last work concerned microwaves, which he rightly believed held the secret of television, Marconi did not forget his first love and his first concern, the sea and those who sailed on it. As early as 1934 he had demonstrated his microwave radio beacon for ship navigation, realizing that these ultra-short waves are ideal for application to radio beacons. At first he confined himself to devising a harbour direction-finder, since he never believed in running (scientifically speaking) before he could walk. During his earliest tests of the Pope's private microwave radio-telephone link at the Vatican, it had been noticed by one of the operators in Rome that each day at the same time a strange noise came over on his receiver, 'something like the sizzle produced by someone walking across slushy ground'. Its appearance was brief but regular, and Marconi quickly discovered it coincided with the passing by the station of a gardener with his cart. What was happening was that this movement passed broadside through the transmitted microwaves, reflecting them back to the receiver. Later, Marconi obtained the same effect using a car, and also a plane in flight. It confirmed his suspicion that it might be possible purposely to bounce back very short waves from solid objects in their path, and this gave him the idea of his harbour direction-finder.

Quite simply, he created a narrow zone of silence at the centre of a beam of waves sent out from a station mounted on shore in a direct line with the centre of the harbour entrance. This beam of signals, with its silent central zone, is then swung continuously from left to right, emitting a high note at the left, and a low note at the right, the change from one signal to the other occurring when the zone of silence exactly coincides with the centre of the harbour entrance. By keeping

Marconi with some of the *Elettra* transmitting apparatus.

his ship exactly on this central zone, a ship's navigator could enter the harbour with complete confidence in darkness or fog, noting the signal changes by loudspeaker or radio-telephone, or visually by the swinging needle of a galvanometer. Marconi outlined and tried this system in 1935, later extending it to range-finding by a ship whose navigator could measure by stop-watch the time elapsing between his receipt of radio and acoustic signals transmitted from the shore simultaneously. He suggested the use, too, of a rotating radio beacon, whose change of tone could be measured on board ship, which would thus have a continuous picture of its bearings relative to the harbour mouth. Marconi firmly believed that such an application of radio would prove of great service to shipping, particularly to coastal and ferry services. Unfortunately he did not live long enough to see its basic principles used in World War

II by Sir Robert Watson-Watt to perfect the device we call radar, with its infinite usefulness not only to all ships everywhere, but to aircraft as well.

Guglielmo Marconi was now back in Italy for good, and spent most of his time in the hands of his doctors who tried, not too successfully, to impose a strict régime on his life. He succumbed again to his earlier, crippling illness of angina pectoris, and although he still managed some travelling, it was clear to those about him that his days were numbered. The end came, quite peacefully, on 20 July 1937, when the weakened heart of the 'pale, calm, kind, meticulous' man beat no more as he tried to turn over in his sick-bed in his house in Rome. His body lay in state for a time, during which many thousands of his fellow-countrymen paid him their last tribute, and he was given a State funeral by the Italian Government. In the words of one onlooker, 'those who saw the procession say that they haver *never* on any occasion in Rome seen anything to equal it. The dense crowds stood for hours and hours in the heat – the heart and soul of Rome, and the whole nation seemed to go with him. It was the humble, loving thought that was so impressive.' At his own wish he was buried in his native Bologna.

But there was also paid a tribute even more moving and more fitting to the memory of the man who had given the world radio. For parallel with his later work there had grown up during his own lifetime the whole vast era of broadcasting as we know it today, and which for most people is the chief application of the words 'wireless' or 'radio'. From spare and primitive beginnings had grown up the world-wide network of radio links, not for the purposes of commerce, marine navigation or the sending of individual personal messages, but for the dissemination of knowledge, information, news, music and entertainment that nowdays buzzes hourly in half-a-hundred different tongues from countless sources the world over.

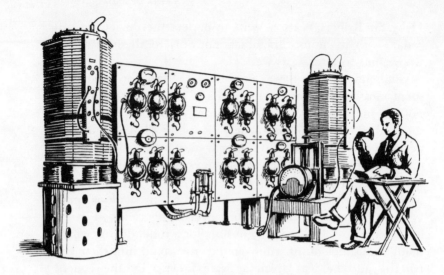

Broadcasting from Chelmsford with a 6-kilowatt transmitter, 1920.

Way back in 1914, after a little demonstration of radio telephony between two buildings in London was given to a distinguished audience by Marconi, a great expert said to him: 'What is the use of telephony? Telegraphy can do it in a more certain way.' Far-sighted as ever, Marconi replied: 'Perhaps some day everyone will have a receiver in their house and, from a central station, news of all kinds will be constantly sent out – telephony will be more useful for that than telegraphy.' The 'soft musical voice' once again had silenced a rigid-minded critic, and this particular ideal was not long in arriving.

In 1920 many interesting experiments were made privately using Marconi equipment, but the first regular broadcast service in Britain, under the control of the General Post Office, began on 14 February 1922, from a place called Writtle, near Chelmsford. The transmitting power was limited to 250 watts, the wave-length to be used was fixed at 400 metres, and broadcasting was permitted between 8.0 and 8.30 p.m. once a week on Tuesday evenings! This station, called 2MT, was run as a sideline by Marconi engineers, and soon gave place to the more famous 2LO station at Marconi House, in London, which began operations in May 1922 on 360 metres. At first, its transmissions were pre-arranged for particular audiences, like hospital patients, society members, fetes, and the like, and over fifty of them were transmitted during that historic year. As 1922 drew to a close, the British Broadcasting Company Ltd, formed by six of the largest manufacturers of wireless equipment, including Marconi's, took over responsibility for what went out from 2LO each evening. By 1926, this was found to be inadequate for the now greatly increased demand for broadcast programmes, and on 1 January 1927 there came into being the British Broadcasting Corporation, a public authority under a royal charter.

Broadcasting on a nationwide scale was then assured in Britain, but it had already gained a firm hold in many other countries, especially in the USA, where since about 1920, large

The first London broadcasting station, 2LO, at Marconi House, London, 1922.

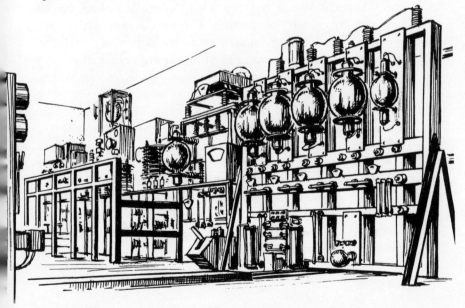

Masts and aerials at the Marconi Beam Station, Bridgwater, Somerset, 1926.

numbers of commercial advertising companies had used the ether to boost their wares – as they still do in that land, as in many others. Although reception in people's homes was at first sketchy, chiefly with the aid of crystal sets with headphones, broadcasting improved technically very quickly, in fact before the content of the programmes reached today's generally very high standards in most parts of the world. Nevertheless, for the last fifteen years or so of Marconi's life, it was evident to him what an enormous effect his invention was already having upon the lives, enlightenment and happiness of millions of people all over the world. It was a staggering achievement to witness in one's own lifetime, and Marconi never ceased to be impressed by it, just as he was never prouder than at having indirectly saved so much life and suffering on the sea.

Anyway, when the news of his death crackled through the ether that hot summer's day in 1937, telling all the world that the legendary Marconi had passed away and would make no more discoveries to aid mankind's onward progress, the very least they could do was to make a gesture – by silence – to his memory. All the BBC and GPO radio transmitters, followed by those in many other countries, went off the air for two minutes beginning at 6.0 p.m. Operators stood at attention beside their apparatus, switchboard girls at international radio-telephone exchanges rose and stood with bowed heads at their places. No wireless messages were received or transmitted during that brief silence. To mark the greatness of the one man who, more than any other, had lifted the huge silence that for centuries had hung over human communication, this short silence stilled the busy air to remind mankind of how much was owed to him.

7

Marconi
the Man

What sort of man was Marconi? Although in his sixty-three years he met and was associated with a great many people, he was not an easy man to know, always the introvert type, sufficient to himself, hard to understand. Yet, so great was his zeal for work and scientific discovery, he possessed an infectious quality that few of his closest helpers could resist. Men like Kemp, Paget, Franklin, Vyvyan and Matthieu were utterly devoted to him, unswerving in their affection and concern that he should be assisted to the very limit.

As a boy, in the secluded early Italian days, Guglielmo Marconi was intensely shy and withdrawn, terribly over-awed by his rather unbending father, finding solace only in his mother, always mischievous, rebellious, intent on his own way. Something of these early traits remained with the man always, and although in the latter half of his life he enjoyed much gaiety and popularity, he never approached the hail-fellow-well-met type. His roots were buried too deep for that. He never lost his inborn desire to withdraw into himself whenever he wanted to – fortunately for us, of course, for where a lesser man might have frittered away years in social trivialities and the idle pursuit of pleasure, Marconi, although he was no spoil-sport, preferred work to the often fruitless seeking of happiness.

Of course, some of his enemies, or those who sought in the early days to exploit him, mistook this quietness and shyness for weakness. But they were wrong. Behind Guglielmo

Marconi's façade of calm and withdrawal lay great strength and determination, as well as untiring energy and an almost superhuman refusal to be downcast by setbacks. With his always lean figure, rather distinguished bearing, piercing eyes and general quietness, he faced innumerable difficulties always with the same taciturnity. One of his associates, the ever-loyal Paget, recounted the fateful happenings on 12 December 1901 at Signal Hill, Newfoundland, and described how even then Marconi showed no outward elation when the first faint signals came through over the ocean. 'He was never unduly elated and never unduly depressed. When the 20 masts erected at Poldhu for the transatlantic transmission collapsed in a gale Marconi looked at the wreckage and said quietly to me: "Well, they will be built again." That was all.'

Such a man tends to inspire others with his own inner zeal, even though they may occasionally miss the more usual outward display of emotion. Thomas A. Edison said of the young Marconi, after he met him for the first time in America: 'He looks like a good man to get along with,' and he was right. In such a complex and difficult field as world radio communications it is quite impossible for one man to do all the work single-handed, and just as he benefited greatly from the previous researches of others, so he knew where to turn for aid. In spite of his natural self-centredness and introversion, not the least of Marconi's achievements was to select the right men to inspire so vividly that they would give him just the help he needed. He invariably managed to fire all those closely associated with his experiments, with the same enthusiasm that he himself was always gripped by.

He has been rightly described as 'the last survivor of the romantic age in science', pioneering in the nineteenth century when rugged individualism was still a potent force in research. Certainly his was the last single-handed mechanical achievement in the sense that he conducted his own experiments and in the early days, at least, made his own apparatus. That kind

Marconi, Kemp and Paget re-united in 1929 on the twenty-eighth
anniversary of the first transatlantic wireless message.

of personal work in science is now over. The amateur is of far
less importance. This is the age of specialists relying upon
mass effort and mass production of equipment, each contri-
buting something to the final discovery, none making individual discoveries of the kind that Faraday, Edison, Bell,
Lodge, and Marconi did.

Marconi always considered himself an amateur of science,
if not of radio manufacture, and in that lay his immense value
to humanity. He knew the limitations of his scientific training,
and relied heavily (and successfully) upon an intuitive sense
that what he believed in would in fact work. Had he been
more of a scientist and less of an amateur discoverer, he might
well have concluded that his critics were right in their scepticism, and done little. He would not have attempted to span
the Atlantic by his crude waves, for instance. Nor would he
have persevered with short-wave transmission over global

distances. As the American radio historian, Professor E.H. Armstrong, of Columbia University, so rightly declared: 'But like all the discoverers who have pushed forward the frontiers of human knowledge, he refused to be bound by other men's reasoning. He went on with his experiments; and he discovered how, by attaching his transmitted waves to the surface of the earth, he could prevent them from travelling in straight lines, and make them slide over the horizon so effectively that in time they joined the continents of the world. Several years were to pass before agreement was reached on the nature of Marconi's great discovery, though Marconi himself understood very well how to apply it and to employ it successfully; and it proved to be the foundation upon which the practical art of wireless signalling was built.'

At one time, his method of communication was always known as 'Marconi's wireless', but he was one of those rare men to become a myth during his own lifetime and his invention a commonplace thing all over the world. This is always the case – as it assuredly was in his – when an originator's original fame is dwarfed by the sheer immensity and perpetuity of his achievement.

Once the initial doubts as to the worth of wireless were dispelled, people in all civilized countries honoured Marconi in abundance. He was awarded the Nobel Prize for physics in 1909, the coveted British awards of the Albert Medal of the Royal Society of Arts and the Kelvin Medal, and honorary degrees and awards from half a dozen countries and sovereigns. Few gave him so much pride, however, as those bestowed upon him by his own beloved Italy – the Freedom of Rome (1903), his appointment as a senator in that country's Senate (1914), and his creation as an hereditary *Marchese* (Marquis) in 1929. As Marchese Marconi he assumed in the last years of his life an aura of special distinction in countries other than his homeland, but he wore it, as he accepted all his many awards, with his innate modesty and calmness.

Someone with so many strange and rewarding assets cannot be expected to have been perfect, and considerable criticism can be levelled at Marconi, at least during most of his years of maturity, on the grounds that his total absorption with his work and himself did not always make for the happiest of personal relationships. There were times when he seemed completely insensitive to the feelings and cares of those close to him, carrying on with his aims and work with almost callous obliviousness. Yet he was not a truly insensitive man.

When old Giuseppe Marconi, his father, died in 1904 it was found he had left the Villa Grifone not to the two elder sons but to Guglielmo, who kept on the estate of so many memories for the rest of his life. Marconi married twice. His first bride was an Irish heiress, the Hon. Beatrice O'Brien, daughter of Lord Inchiquin, an Irish peer. He met and married her in 1905, at the height of his early fame, but although there were two girls and a boy of this marriage, it did not prove lastingly happy and was dissolved in 1927, in which year he married the Contessa Maria Cristina Bezzi-Scali, the daughter of a Vatican nobleman and his equally aristocratic Roman wife. There was one child of this second marriage, a daughter whom Marconi named Elettra, after his yacht. Annie Marconi, the mother whose early support and encouragement had meant so much to Guglielmo when he was young and unknown, lived on into her eighties and died in Italy in 1920, but since her son had become famous and much given to world travelling, he had grown away from her and did not even attend her funeral. Her last years were comforted by the devoted care of her first-born son, Alfonso, who himself died in 1936.

The other accusation that can and must be levelled against this otherwise always oddly likable man is that he seemed to have pro-Fascist leanings. At any rate, he early supported the dictatorial régime of Benito Mussolini in Italy, sincerely believing it to be the one force that would save from dissension and collapse the country he loved so much. If it now seems

Marconi and his wife on the bridge of the *Elettra*, 1934.

that Marconi's ever-powerful patriotism blinded him to the
evil of Mussolini, it must also be recorded that the dictator
himself, anxious to gain this famous Italian's support, carefully wooed him, gave him governmental support, and for a
time cultivated him as a personal friend. For instance,
Mussolini treated the inventor on a comradely level, showed
a constant interest in radio development, and frequently
visited the *Elettra*, often informally. Marconi had no real
political leanings, but he liked being listened to by his country's dynamic ruler. 'I am not a political man,' he once
declared. In fact, he was a political innocent, and disillusion
came to him before he died, notably over the Abyssinian war
in 1935.

Although Guglielmo inherited from his father the sound
business sense that was so important in his work, he was not
particularly good at handling money on a personal level. The
man who, right from the very beginning, had seen the potential commercial value of wireless and had built up the great

concern that bore his name, with its many associate firms all over the globe, hated making hard-and-fast financial arrangements himself. With his undoubted personal extravagance during the latter half of his life, he was not always as well-off as he should have been, and for a time his first wife and her children were left without the adequate monetary provision he had promised them. What did never leave him, and in fact grew with the years, was his innate sense of showmanship. There was an embryo showman demonstrating his apparatus to British Government officials before the turn of the century, and most of Marconi's later exploits were handled with brilliant showmanship and what is now called a sense of publicity value. In fact, towards the end of his life, Marconi seemed to enjoy being a public figure – without losing his need for seclusion.

One incident in Marconi's life may have had some bearing on his later character: certainly it might have discouraged and unduly depressed a lesser man. In 1911, whilst driving his brand-new Fiat car with his wife and a chauffeur from Pisa to Genoa, he collided with another car on a hair-pin bend. No one was seriously hurt save Marconi himself. His right eye was injured and had to be removed, and the sight of the other was only saved at the last moment by the skill of the surgeons. He later wore a glass eye.

If Marconi could be cold as well as warm-hearted, could rarely suffer fools gladly and could on occasion be very rude to those who bored him or wasted his time, there was another side to the man that needs to be mentioned. Many people felt him a difficult man to get along with, but those who did penetrate his steely mask found a delightful companion. As his great friend and associate, Luigi Solari, said: 'In intimate circles and with trusted friends he displayed a simple and youthful joy which was very surprising to people who had only met him at official meetings.' He loved sailing and motor-boating, he always enjoyed motoring, in spite of his accident, and in earlier years he enjoyed shooting, fishing and cycling. Anything mechanical appealed to him, and he had a sense of humour that was at once simple and highly individual and which appealed very much to children. When his own children were young he would often play trains or boats with them, and it remains one of the tragedies of his life that with increasing pressure of radio work, he enjoyed less and less family life as his first three children began to grow up.

Another interest that lay deep in his nature but which also never received the time it needed to develop fully was music. As a young man, trained by his singer mother, Marconi was an accomplished pianist, often accompanying her or playing duets with her. It is probable that had not a greater love for science intervened he might well have become a professional musician.

Yet with all his gifts of perseverance and a liking for constant hard work, his 'solemn and ponderous attention to detail', his self-confidence, ingenuity as an inventor and untiring energy, his commercial flair and the rare ability to inspire other people, Guglielmo Marconi would never have been the great world figure he was without one other immense asset: his foresight. It was his vision of radio as a vital factor in modern human life that led him on to greatness. In the words of G. R. M. Garratt: 'Of all those who had blazed the trail he alone had the vision to see the practical application. Where others had seen only a new and interesting scientific phenomenon, Marconi saw its practical utility.'

Perhaps, too, his vision extended further than that. In a rare moment of self-revelation he once said, in public: 'The more a man bends the phenomena of nature to his will the more he discovers and the more he will continue to discover. Because of this he will increasingly realize the infinity of the Infinite.'

8

What We Owe
to Marconi

Although some aspect of radio, in its manifold forms, or of its latest development, television, plays a regular part in the lives of almost everyone in the world either directly or indirectly these days, it does require a little imagination to see the immensity of the debt we owe to Marconi. The whole process of communicating through space, talking at a distance by electro-magnetic waves, nowadays seems so simple, so foolproof, so much a part of the modern world, that it is hard not to take it very much for granted. If every form of radio were to be suddenly taken away from us, our bustling modern world would instantly grind to an ignominious halt.

Yet as we watched Guglielmo Marconi follow his obsessive idea from boyhood in secluded obscurity to universal fame and eminence, stumbling step by painful step towards the truth he knew he must discover and which has now become an almost unnoticed part of our daily lives, no matter who or where we are, it is important to see him as one of a line of scientific discoverers, as well as an individual man who gave human civilization a new and upward turn. Although himself not a great innovator, nor even a brilliant mechanical inventor, he nevertheless rightly belongs to a continuous stream of great men whose labours benefit us now.

One day well over a century ago, in 1846, a famous discoverer was due to lecture at the Royal Institution, in London, and all that afternoon he had been helped get his apparatus ready by the resident lecturer there, the great English scientist, Michael Faraday. At the last moment the man's courage failed him and he did not turn up to give his lecture. Rather than disappoint the audience, Faraday delivered the talk from material he had or could remember, but he finished before time and could not recall any more to complete the few minutes of the time allotted. So, instead, Faraday spoke about some thoughts of his own that had lately impressed themselves on his mind on the way in which electricity is propagated through space. He called his own little talk 'Thoughts on Ray Vibrations', and later contributed a technical paper of the same title to the *Philosophical Magazine*. Among the readers of that learned journal, although he was then only a boy of fifteen, was James Clerk Maxwell, and it was on Faraday's ideas that Maxwell later based his own theory of electromagnetic waves, of which his mathematical development was so ingenious.

Long afterwards, in 1937, shortly after the death of Marconi, Sir William Bragg and some other scientists at the Royal Society, in London, decided to open a packet of old letters that had lain for a great many years in the safe there, some of them curiously marked: 'Sealed: not to be opened at present.' One of them was written by Faraday a century before, in 1832, in which he said: 'I cannot but think that the action of electricity and magnetism is propagated through space in some form of vibration.' His idea of vibration was clearly very close to our modern conception of waves, and this was the germ of the idea that spurred Maxwell on to his theory, and led directly to the work of Hertz, Lodge, Righi, and so to that of Marconi. He was in direct line with such earlier pioneers, just as his own work was in its turn followed with equal success by men like Fleming, Baird, and Watson-Watt. Whether or not they are widely known, all these men were benefactors of mankind by their efforts at extending the scope of human communications.

117

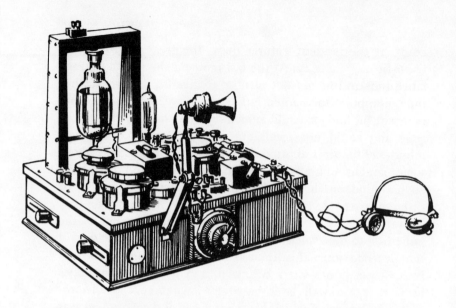

Experimental wireless telephone set used by Marconi and Round in 1914.

At first, the use of wireless was largely confined to the sending of telegraphic messages for business, private or official purposes, and to aid ships at sea. Radio telegraphy and telephony continues to be a vastly important part of the development of Marconi's work, and quite apart from all radio broadcasting, there crackles through the ether today a ceaseless flow of such messages, directly by voice where this is necessary, or in Morse or one or other of the various international codes now in use, some secret, that one could say, without exaggeration, help to keep the world's wheels turning smoothly. The entire globe is covered by a buzzing network of radio communication channels, all carefully worked out and many of them operated by the governments of the various countries, all using short-wave directional beam systems. At least six such channels link Britain with North and South America, while there are direct and permanent radio links between most of the capitals of the world, from London to Tokyo, Paris to Caracas, Cape Town to Moscow, Ottawa to Bangkok. Even the vast open expanse of the Pacific Ocean is spanned by linked radio channels far beyond the wildest dreams of the early pioneers. These days a 'scrambling device', which ensures that anyone other than the intended recipient will hear nothing but a jumbled mass of sounds, is in general use on all radio-telephone links.

To marine wireless we must now add radio used by aircraft, and to both must also be added the invaluable navigational aid of radar. These two uses are now so universal that no one in his right mind would undertake any voyage or flight by sea or air of any length in ship or plane not equipped with radio. Indeed, without both radio and radar, navigation as such would today seem as primitive as that relied upon by Columbus. In addition, short-wave radio links are everyday practice

Marconi direction-finding aerial installed on an airport control tower.

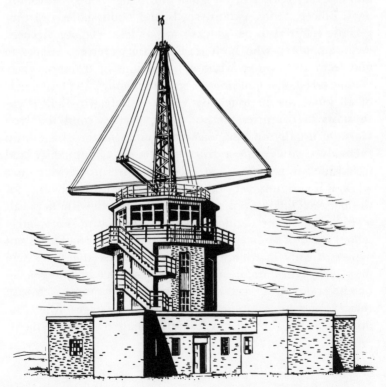

on land as well, whether they aid police cars on patrol, city taxis plying for hire, long-distance railway expresses, walkie-talkie systems, troops on manœuvres, or whatever.

Right from the very earliest days of wireless communication, long before the term 'radio' (derived from *radiated* waves) came into more or less general use, mechanically-minded people in all walks of life and in many different countries were fired by the magic of it all, and wanted to play with waves themselves. In a sense Marconi was the very first radio amateur, and soon after he succeeded in spanning the Atlantic with his apparatus, many others wanted to set up similar, even equal links by wireless. From the very beginning, as we have seen, they were officially allotted the seemingly useless short-wave bands only, and before long 'ham' radio, as it is known today, became firmly established as a hobby with a difference. Now, in almost every corner of the globe, in living-rooms, bedrooms, dens, offices, attics, cabins, sheds and cubby-holes (all universally referred to as 'shacks') are at least 260,000 licensed radio amateurs, who both transmit and receive messages to and from each other without restrictions of distance, race, colour, creed, age, politics or sex. Daily, hourly in fact, 'hams' of all kinds are in touch by voice or code with fellow enthusiasts in countries far and near, even beyond the Iron Curtain, usually on low-powered equipment they have built themselves, always in a true, keen spirit of humanity and friendship. If not the most spectacular result of Marconi's work, it is certainly very far from being the least valuable, for this personal linkage represents an achievement without parallel in human history, added to which is the fine and completely selfless spirit of service that all true 'hams' possess. This is not expressed only in friendly messages and trivial talk, but in many very real humane acts – offering service in emergencies like flood or storm, keeping remote Servicemen in touch with their homes and families, transmitting messages where no others can get through, even aiding their own governments in service and security work. The world's 'hams', with their terrific zest for their highly fascinating hobby, are a truly dedicated group whose unheralded work for peace and human friendship cannot be over-estimated.

But for most of us, of course, the main debt we owe to Marconi's tireless work lies in our ability to hear and see broadcast radio and TV programmes. It is impossible, at this late date, to gauge exactly the impact ordinary radio broadcasting has had upon human progress and the onward march of civilization. One can only say that it has been tremendous and far-reaching. To millions of people, first with their crude crystal sets, then with their simple valve receivers and big horn loudspeakers, and now with their compact portable sets, hi-fi receivers, pocket transistors and car radios, broadcast sound has long been an indispensable part of life itself. The achievement of the BBC, followed if not matched by every other country in the world, shows just how education, enlightenment and entertainment can all come into people's homes to their lasting benefit. There is hardly any form of human thought or experience not covered by radio programmes today, and even apart from the directly educational programmes aimed at schools or adult groups, the widespread dissemination of news, information and thought, much aided by talks and discussion programmes, has had an immeasurable effect upon the world as we know it today.

Of course, like everything else used by man, broadcasting can be a force for good or ill, and it would be absurd to ignore its harmful side. In sponsored programmes such as those broadcast in thousands every day in the USA, the listener is subjected to little more than intrusive paid-for advertising. But much more sinister is the vast power of radio as a political force – when used by corrupt governments. It is no exaggeration to say that Hitler's rise to power in Germany was achieved only with the aid of broadcasting, for his harsh, mesmeric voice, heard direct by the few thousands present at

Modern high-frequency Marconi transmitter used by the BBC.

his meetings and rallies, was invariably broadcast to, and made compulsory listening for, many other millions of people. In the 1930s the German people were in fact hypnotized by radio waves. Similarly, a ceaseless flow of false political propaganda put out day after day to millions of listeners by known or even anonymous speakers can have a like effect, as we have seen not only in Germany, but in Marconi's native Italy, in Japan, Russia, the Near East, and elsewhere. On the other hand, truthful news and facts broadcast may have the reverse effect, as was particularly seen during World War II, when the regular broadcasts from London to the occupied peoples and resistance groups all over Europe kept the heart of freedom alive and immeasurably helped to overthrow the tyranny that then threatened the world.

Nor should we under-estimate radio's potential for both good and evil today. Nor, on a universally happier note, should we ever forget the vast service a musical young Italian's work performed for the cause of the best international language of all, music. Not until the coming of broadcasting, with its ceaseless fountain-head of music of every possible kind, did ordinary people everywhere know so much music, know so much about it, or gain so much enjoyment from it.

As for television, it is clear that Marconi always regarded the transmission of pictures with sound as a logical development of ordinary radio. In his later work on the ultra-short waves he foresaw that only by their use could high definition television pictures be developed on any scale as a public service. This is because a large frequency band-width is necessary and so the longer waves cannot be used. With the eventual development of colour television, the new medium clearly looks like having an even greater effect upon the future of mankind than did what we now affectionately call 'steam radio'. And with the use of more TV space satellites like Telstar and Early Bird, the distance difficulties with TV will doubtless soon be completely overcome. Already, thanks to these satellites' miraculous aid, Marconi's 1901 feat has been paralleled in pictures, viewers in America seeing on their screens events as they actually happen in Britain, and vice versa.

The latest development in radio – but obviously not the last – is its striking application to space research. Coded signal impulses and television pictures sent out from satellites and space craft using solar batteries keep these man-made explorers into space in close touch with the earth by using the same electric impulses as first throbbed across the attic room at Pontecchio, but the distances they cover reach out far beyond anything Marconi could have envisaged. Nor could he have foreseen the development of gigantic radio telescope listening devices to pick up the faint but certain sounds from outer space, scanning the earthly sky like enormous, ever-waiting ears. Already a space craft has sent back data about

123

the planet Venus from a distance of 35 million miles, and when the first men land on the moon, on Mars and beyond, they too will be in constant touch with the earth through the universal significance of radio. As the earth has long been shrunken by the wonder of radio communication, and men no longer isolated from one another by mere intervening distance, so in time the vastness of space will be reduced and men will talk across unimaginable distances, thanks largely to the endlessly beneficial labours of Guglielmo Marconi.

No wonder *The Times* said in its obituary of him: 'When the twentieth century comes to be surveyed by historians yet unborn, Guglielmo Marconi may be regarded as the supremely significant character of our epoch.'

Table of Dates

1865   James Clerk Maxwell proves mathematically the existence of electro-magnetic waves in space.

1874   Guglielmo Marconi born at Bologna, Italy, 25 April.

1887   Heinrich Herz detects and produces radio waves.

1890   Edouard Branly invents the coherer detector.

1894–5   Marconi carries out his first original experiments in wireless telegraphy, transmitting up to 2 miles.

1896   Marconi begins work in England: Patent No. 12039 granted.

1897   Radio contact is established across the Bristol Channel, $8\frac{1}{4}$ miles. Marconi forms his own company.

1898   The world's first paid wireless telegram is sent by Lord Kelvin, from the Isle of Wight to Bournemouth, $18\frac{1}{2}$ miles.

1899   Marconi established the first radio link between England and France.

1900   The 'Four Sevens' Patent, No. 7777. The Poldhu station established.

1901   The Atlantic is bridged by radio, 2,170 miles, 12 December.

1907   The first transoceanic radio service between Glace Bay, Nova Scotia, and Clifden, Ireland.

1912   The *Titanic* disaster, 14 April.

1916–7   Marconi begins work on short waves.

1920–4   Marconi starts short-wave experiments from the *Elettra*.

1934–5   Marconi demonstrates microwave radio beacon for harbour direction-finding and ship navigation.

1937   Marconi dies in Rome, 20 July.

Suggestions for Further Reading

Marconi – Master of Space. B. L. Jacot and D. M. B. Collier, Hutchinson, 1935.

My Father, Marconi. Degna Marconi, McGraw-Hill, 1962.

Telegraphy. J. W. Freebody, Pitman, 1959.

Radio Today. D. K. McCleery, Oxford University Press, 1961.

Electronics for Everyone (The Story of Electricity in Action: Television, Radio, Radar, High Fidelity, etc.). Monroe Upton, Faber, 1956.

Communications in Space (From Wireless to Satellite Relay). Orrin E. Dunlap, Jnr., Harper & Row, 1962.

Index

127